MYTHS AND LEGENDS
OF THE GREEKS

MYTHS AND LEGENDS
OF THE GREEKS

BY NICOLA ANN SISSONS

ILLUSTRATED BY RAFAELLO BUSONI

Hart Publishing Company

NEW YORK CITY

CONTENTS

List of Illustrations

THE WINGED HORSE

The Killing of a Chimaera

IN ANCIENT DAYS there was a wonderful white horse called Pegasus. He spent most of his time on the slopes of Mount Helicon, but he could fly through the air like an eagle, for he had beautiful silver wings. He was wild and swift, and had never been ridden or bridled by anyone.

One moonlight night, Pegasus came down to the meadows which lay at the foot of Mount Helicon. Here he struck the ground with his hoof, and immediately a beautiful fountain gushed forth. Pegasus drank of its magic water, and then flew off again above the clouds.

People called it the Fountain of Hippocrene, and often shepherds used to come there at full moon to catch a glimpse of the wonderful Pegasus, who came from time to time to drink at the fountain.

Now a certain country was being laid waste in Asia by a terrible monster called a chimaera. It had three heads—those of a lion, a goat, and a snake—and its body and feet were like those of a dragon. Fire and smoke came from its three great mouths, which were so huge that they looked like enormous caves.

The king of that country had asked a young hero called Bellerophon to catch the Winged Pegasus, so that with this wonderful horse he might kill the hateful chimaera. So, night after night, Bellerophon watched at the fountain for Pegasus; but he was never fortunate enough to see the horse, though once he fancied he heard the sound of his silver wings.

One night, however, he arrived later than usual at the fountain, having taken a little lost child to a shepherd's hut for safety from wild animals. To his joy he saw Pegasus alight on the meadow. After drinking some of the water, the horse began to caper about in a playful mood.

Presently Pegasus caught sight of Bellerophon and flew off immediately, far above the clouds. To catch him was impossible, so Bellerophon, weary with watching, lay down to sleep.

As he slept, the Goddess Minerva brought a wonderful golden bridle, set with precious stones, and placed it in his hand. When he awoke he knew that with this magic bridle he would be able to tame Pegasus.

That night he hid himself again by the fountain. Soon Pegasus came winging in great circles towards the earth, and alighted so gently that scarcely a blade of grass moved.

He came towards Bellerophon and lowered his head for the bridle, which was soon put in its place. Then Pegasus became suddenly tamed and Bellerophon sprang quickly on to his back. In a moment they soared up and above the clouds.

Bellerophon soon grew used to flying through the air, and he guided his swift steed to the mountain of the monster, chimaera, which lay in the midst of waste land.

Smoke and fire were coming from its hideous mouths, but Pegasus swooped down quickly, and Bellerophon struck the goat's head a mighty blow with his sword.

In a flash it had rolled on to the ground, while Pegasus shot upward again out of reach of the other two heads, which roared and hissed in a dreadful way.

One more dash down, and the lion's head was cut off. A third time Pegasus swooped down, and Bellerophon slashed off the snake's head.

So the terrible chimaera was killed, and the people

. . . Pegasus swooped down quickly, and Bellerophon struck the goat's head . . .

rejoiced that now the land was safe and they would
be able to grow corn and grapevines once more and
live happily without fear of the chimaera.

THE GOLDEN APPLE

A Prize for the Fairest

LONG AGO, A great wedding feast was being given amongst the gods. It was a very special occasion because a sea nymph was going to marry a mortal. All the gods and goddesses of Olympia were invited to the wedding—with one exception.

The Goddess Eris was not asked. Because she always made people quarrel wherever she went, she was called the Goddess of Discord. For that reason, no one wanted to invite her to any feasts.

When she found out about the feast and discovered that she had not been invited to the wedding, the Goddess Eris was very angry indeed. She decided to cause as much trouble as she possibly could and she soon hit upon an idea that was certain to cause discord among the goddesses.

While the guests were enjoying the feast, Eris threw a golden apple amongst them. On the apple were written the words: FOR THE FAIREST.

Exactly as Eris had foreseen, quarreling immediately broke out amongst the goddesses as to which was the fairest among them and, therefore, which one of them should receive the honor of being presented with the apple.

At last it was decided that the three most beautiful goddesses were: Venus, the Goddess of Beauty; Juno, the Queen of Heaven; and Athena, the Goddess of Wisdom.

No one, not even the gods themselves, dared to risk the anger of these great beauties by saying who was the fairest. Finally, the gods decided to ask a young shepherd who tended the sheep on Mount Ida to be the judge. The shepherd's name was Paris.

When the three goddesses ranged themselves before Paris to be judged, the first one to speak was Juno.

She said to Paris, "If you give the apple to me, I will promise you great riches, and one day you shall be King."

Then came Athena, saying, "If you give me the apple, I will grant you wisdom to the end of your days."

Last of all came Venus. Paris had been tormented by

. . . the goddesses ranged themselves before Paris
to be judged . . .

trying to make a choice as to which was the more beautiful—Juno or Athena. But when he saw Venus he was amazed at her beauty; and well he might be, for she was by far the most beautiful.

Venus said quietly, "Give me the apple, Paris, and you shall have the fairest woman in the world for your wife." Paris handed her the apple.

In spite of the fact that Venus was the Goddess of Beauty, she was greatly pleased with Paris for awarding the golden apple to her and promised him that she would always be his friend. Then she told him that although he had been brought up as a shepherd that he was really the son of Priam, King of Troy, and that one day he would have a noblewoman for his bride.

Not long afterwards, Paris set sail for Greece. Eventually he reached the court of King Menelaus of Sparta; there Paris saw the King's beautiful wife, Helen.

Helen was indeed the most beautiful woman in the whole world, and it was not long before Paris fell deeply in love with her. Paris saw much of the beautiful Helen and one day when the King was occupied with his soldiers, Paris persuaded Helen to run off with him.

The lovers sailed away to Troy. When King Menelaus returned to court and found that his wife had eloped, he was exceedingly angry. Immediately he ordered ships to be made ready to take an army to Troy and bring Helen back to her rightful husband.

It was the King of Sparta's efforts to regain his wife that started the famous Trojan war which raged for nine long years—but that is another story which can be read about later in this book.

THE FAITHFUL COUPLE

A Tale of Kindness Rewarded

ONCE UPON A time, Jupiter, the king of the gods, and his son, Mercury, were traveling on the earth disguised as ordinary mortals. To everyone, they looked like just an old man and his son.

One evening, they came to a village. They knocked on the door of a house and asked for food and shelter.

"We are weary and hungry," they said. "Perhaps you can help us."

"It's late. Go away!" came the answer.

In such a selfish and unkind way, they were turned away from house after house.

At last they came to a little, thatch-roofed cottage

outside of the town. A poor old man and his wife lived here. This old couple knew what it was to be tired and hungry. All their lives, they had worked hard. They lived simply, as best they could, and instead of being bitter and envious of other people's wealth, they sympathized with their fellow men.

To this humble house came the two gods, still disguised as ordinary mortals. With kindness, the old wife, whose name was Baucis, welcomed them in.

The old man, Philemon, spread a cloth over a rickety bench, and asked them to sit down. He warmed some water for them to wash the dust of the roads off their hands. Baucis set to work immediately to prepare the best meal that she could.

It was a simple meal, not at all like the fine food that the gods usually ate. The wine was new and sour, not old and mellow, but it was the best that the old couple had. And while the gods were waiting for the meal to be cooked, the old couple's pleasant conversation made the time pass quickly.

Then they all sat down together in a happy mood. But gradually, Baucis and Philemon began to notice something strange — the more wine they poured into the cups, the more wine there seemed to be in the pitcher. Suddenly, they realized that these were not poor travelers, but gods.

They fell on their knees and begged forgiveness that they had offered such poor hospitality to Jupiter and Mercury.

"Oh, no," said Jupiter. "You shared what was your best with humble wayfarers. You did not know who we were, yet you held back nothing from us and treated us with loving kindness. Even the gods themselves could not do more.

"The hardhearted people of your village shall be punished, but you shall be rewarded. Come with us to the top of yonder hill."

So Baucis and Philemon climbed to the top of the hill with them.

"Look," said Jupiter, "such is the fate of your village."

Baucis and Philemon looked down on the valley, and where once was their village, now there was a huge lake. All the houses except their humble cottage were sunk beneath the water.

As they watched, their cottage was transformed into a beautiful temple. The straw roof became a golden roof, and the rickety walls turned into beautiful marble columns.

"Now, Baucis and Philemon, tell us your wishes," said the gods. "Ask what you will, it shall be granted."

Then Baucis and Philemon spoke quietly to each other. They did not have to consult long, for they knew what they wanted.

"Grant us that we may never be separated," they begged. "We have lived our lives together in love

They fell on their knees and begged forgiveness that they had offered such poor hospitality to Jupiter and Mercury.

and peace. Do not let either of us have to bear the sorrow of being left without the other."

Their prayer was granted. Baucis and Philemon lived for many happy years as guardians of the temple.

Then, one day when they were very, very old, they were changed into trees, both at the same moment. To this day, the people who live near that place point to a beautiful old oak tree and a lovely linden growing near a lake, and then they tell the story of Baucis and Philemon.

THE GOLDEN RAM

The Rescue of Two Children

LONG AGO IN Greece there lived a king whose wife, Nephele, was a beautiful cloud nymph. She loved her husband and her son, Phryxus, and her daughter, Helle, but she used to grow so weak and ill when the sunny days came that she felt compelled at these times to leave her home and wander off with the other cloud nymphs.

The king at last grew tired of this, and once when Nephele was away longer than usual, he married Ino, a beautiful, dark-eyed witch maiden. Now Ino treated Phryxus and Helle very cruelly, and the farther the cloud nymphs wandered, the more the children missed their own mother, Nephele. The earth grew parched and dry, for no rain fell when the clouds were away, and soon a terrible famine came upon the land.

Ino made this the excuse for getting rid of the children, saying that Phryxus and Helle must be offered as a sacrifice to turn away the anger of the gods.

So the poor children were brought to the altar, and everything was made ready for sacrifice. But Nephele was watching over them, and from the clouds she sent a golden-fleeced ram, which took them on its back and bore them away.

On and on it flew till it reached a narrow sea. But here Helle grew so weak that she fell from the ram's back and was drowned in the water below, and ever since then the place has been called the Hellespont.

The ram sped on with Phryxus to the land of Colchis, where the boy lived for some time and afterwards married the king's daughter there.

When the ram died, Phryxus hung its beautiful golden fleece upon a branch of the oak tree in the grove of Ares, the War God. It shone so brightly that it lit up the dark forest trees and was the greatest treasure in the land.

No one dared venture near the place, for a terrible dragon was set to guard it night and day.

Even when Phryxus died, and a new king ruled in Colchis, the Golden Fleece still hung on the oak tree,

. . . from the clouds she sent a golden-fleeced ram
which took them on its back and bore them away.

waiting for some hero brave enough to do battle with
the fierce dragon.

ORPHEUS THE SINGER

A Visit to the Underworld

APOLLO, THE LORD of Music, had a son called Orpheus. He was often called the Sweet Singer, and he would wander away to lonely places to play to the creatures there. Lions and bears and wolves stopped their wild ways to listen to him, while little creatures crept near to hear him.

Trees uprooted themselves and made a circle around him so that the hot sun might not hurt him as he played. When he wandered in the valleys, his tunes charmed the beautiful wood nymphs, and in time one of them, called Eurydice, became his wife.

Many happy days they spent together, till once, as

Eurydice was tripping through the meadows, she chanced to step upon a serpent coiled up in the grass. In an instant it reared its head and stung her ankle, and she was carried away by Pluto, the King of the Underworld, to his home in Hades.

Orpheus could not understand what had happened to her, and he searched everywhere for his lost bride, singing his sad, lonely song wherever he went, and calling her name until even the stones and the wild beasts grieved for him.

The gods, too, in Mount Olympus listened to his wailing, but they could not bring Eurydice back, for they had no power over the dwellers in the Underworld.

Having wandered everywhere on earth, Orpheus left the sunny valley and played on until he reached the cave where Pluto rules over the spirits of the dead.

Here his magic music cast a spell over them all, for he sang of youth and love, of the beauty of the earth, and of the sadness of losing Eurydice. Soon the ghostly spirits forgot their own pain in sorrow for him.

When they heard the music from the lyre of the heartbroken Orpheus, all the inhabitants of the Underworld flocked around him.

Young lovers who had been parted by death, brave heroes who had perished in battle, loving parents long separated from their children—all sought comfort from Orpheus's sublime music. The Furies themselves were

*. . . all the inhabitants of the Underworld
flocked around him.*

melted by the strains of his lyre and, for the first time
in the centuries of their existence, they wept. Even the
vultures stopped their perpetual tearing at the vitals of
Prometheus, a thing they had been doing ever since
that giant had been chained to a rock by Jupiter.

Finally Orpheus approached the great throne where
King Pluto and Queen Proserpine sat. To them he sang
his most lovely song in which he told them how love
had brought him to the Underworld in his search for
Eurydice; he implored them to restore his beloved
wife to him.

At last Pluto and his Queen, Proserpine, promised that Eurydice should return with Orpheus, but on one condition; he must have faith to believe that Eurydice was really following him, and on no account was he to look back at her until he had reached the upper air. If he did, she would be drawn back again into the Underworld and be lost to him forever.

Orpheus promised to obey and, hastening upward, he climbed the steep path towards the land of sunshine and light. Eurydice's steps behind him made no sound, and just when he could feel the fresh air of the upper world on his face, his heart sank, for he feared that Pluto might have tricked him after all. He felt that he must know if Eurydice were really following him.

He turned his head. She was there smiling at him. But, alas, he had broken his promise! Although her arms were outstretched towards him, she could not follow him any farther. Slowly she slipped back—back—back—into the Underworld, never to see him again.

So Orpheus had to go on alone. He went to live on a lonely mountain, playing always on his lyre the saddest of music.

When he died, his lyre floated down the river to an island where the nightingales learned its wonderful music, and where to this day they sing more sweetly than anywhere else in the world.

Slowly she slipped back—back—back—
into the Underworld.

PYRAMUS AND THISBE

A Wall Between Two Lovers

MANY YEARS AGO in the city of Babylon, there lived a boy and girl called Pyramus and Thisbe. The boy was exceedingly handsome, his name was Pyramus, while Thisbe was the most beautiful girl in Babylon.

Because they were neighbors, they saw each other constantly, and as they were both such beautiful and endearing youngsters, they very soon fell in love. And, having fallen in love, quite naturally they wanted to get married.

Unfortunately neither of their parents approved of such a marriage. But although the two sets of parents forbade Pyramus and Thisbe to see each other, they could not prevent them from remaining in love.

The houses of the young lovers were divided by a wall. The builders who had constructed this wall had not done their job very well, for they had left a small chink in the brickwork.

The lovers soon found the hole and, to their delight, they found that they could talk to each other through this chink. Every morning Pyramus and Thisbe would rush to his and her side of the wall and they would murmur secret words of love to each other. During the day, if the opportunity arose, they would return to the wall to exchange greetings and to comfort each other over their cruel separation.

When night came they would meet on either side of the wall to bid each other good night and press their kisses against the wall's cold, hard surface. Often when they grew unhappy about their plight they would reproach the wall and say, "O wall! How can you be so cruel to separate us in this way. At least make this hole just a little bigger so that we can kiss each other good night." But of course the wall remained unyielding, and daily the lovers grew more and more unhappy.

Finally Pyramus and Thisbe decided they could bear their separation no longer. Through the chink in the wall they made their plans to run away together. It was decided that they would each make their way to a meeting place just outside the city gates at the tomb

The lovers . . . found they could talk to each other through this chink.

of Ninus. There they could hide in the shade of a mulberry tree with its long hanging branches which swept close to the ground.

One night when both their families and all the servants were fast asleep, Thisbe crept silently out of her house. Drawing a heavy veil over her face, she made her way swiftly to the tomb and hid herself under the branches of the sheltering mulberry tree.

Near to the tree was a small, bubbling spring to which the animals came to quench their thirst when few humans were around. As Thisbe sat there waiting happily for Pyramus, a lioness appeared. She had just killed a young calf and her mouth was smeared with blood. As she made her way to drink at the spring, Thisbe saw the lioness approaching in the moonlight.

Terrified, the girl leaped up and ran for safety to a nearby cave into which she crawled. As she fled, Thisbe dropped the veil with which she had covered her face. After quenching her thirst, the lioness sniffed around and found the veil which she tore to pieces in her rage that she could not find the human to whom it belonged. Her jaws were still bloody and the veil was smeared with blood.

When Pyramus arrived on the scene, the first thing he saw were the footprints of the lioness in the sand. Thisbe was nowhere to be seen! Under the mulberry tree where she should have been, lay her veil—torn and bloody.

Thisbe saw the lioness approaching in the moonlight. Terrified, the girl ran . . .

The unhappy youth cried out in his grief: "This night will make an end of two lovers! It is I who have caused the death of my beloved Thisbe. I should never have asked her to run away with me and leave her family."

He shed tears on the scarf and kissed it tenderly. Then he said to it: "Oh scarf! drink my blood too—for I no longer wish to live."

As he said these words, he plunged the sword—which he carried to ward off wild beasts—into his heart. The blood spurted high into the branches of the mulberry tree and the white berries on the tree were stained a deep red as he lay dying.

Daylight began to approach and with it Thisbe's courage returned. She crept out of the cave, searching for Pyramus. When she came to the tree she was puzzled; the berries which had been white in the moonlight were now a very dark red. While she paused in bewilderment she heard a faint moan from under the tree.

Thisbe lifted the branches and there to her dismay she saw Pyramus prostrate on the ground. She knelt beside him and took him in her arms crying, "Oh Pyramus, my beloved, do not leave me I beg of you. Who has done this terrible thing?"

Pyramus still held her veil clutched in his hand and when Thisbe saw how it was torn and covered with blood she understood what had happened.

"Oh Pyramus," she cried, "Your love has made you take your own life because you thought I no longer lived. I, too, feel that life is worthless without you. I will follow you in death as I would have followed you in life. This tree shall cover us forever."

As she spoke, Thisbe took the sword from Pyramus who was now dead and placed it against her heart. She fell forward on it across the body of Pyramus in a last embrace; her blood soaked into the roots of the tree.

The gods were deeply touched by the tragedy of the young lovers and they decreed that the berries of the tree, which up till then had always been white, would now remain the deep, dark red they had turned with the blood of Pyramus and Thisbe.

THE TROJAN HORSE

The Trick that Won a War

THE FAMOUS Trojan war had been raging for nine long years. The great struggle had started when Paris, son of the king of Troy, had fallen in love with the beautiful Helen, wife of Menelaus, King of Sparta.

Paris kidnapped Helen, and carried her off to Troy. King Menelaus called upon his allies, the kings of all his neighboring countries, to help him rescue his queen. Together, the kings of Greece fitted out an army and set forth to battle against Troy and rescue Helen.

After much fighting, the Greeks finally surrounded the city of Troy. Food became scarce in the city. People

41

were starving, but still the Trojans bravely fought on—
fought on for many long months.

It began to look as though the Greeks would never
conquer Troy. Then Ulysses, the Greek general,
thought of a clever plan. Far from the city, Ulysses commanded his men to build an enormous wooden horse.
Then the Greeks were told to fill the horse with hundreds of armed soldiers.

One night, the Greeks pulled the horse across the
fields and placed it just outside the city walls. Then
they boarded their ships, and sailed a short distance
away so that it would seem as if they had given up
the siege.

The next morning, the watchers on the walls of
Troy let out a cry, "Praise be to Jupiter! The Greeks
have gone! The siege is over! We are saved!"

They threw open the huge gates and the people
rushed out. Oh! how happy they were. Now they
would be able to get food!

When they saw the enormous horse, they asked
each other what it could be. Some of the leaders of
the city said, "Burn it—it is some kind of trick."

Just then a group of Trojan soldiers came along,
dragging a prisoner. They had found a Greek soldier
hiding in the woods nearby. The Greek trembled with
terror and begged the Trojans not to kill him. He said
he had run away from his army because he was certain
that the Greeks were going to lose the war. When

they questioned him about the horse, he told the Trojans that it had been made by the Greeks as an offering to the gods.

"Why," the Trojan commanders demanded to know, "why was the horse built to such an enormous size?" The captured soldier replied that the animal had purposely been made large, so that the Trojans could never take it away from the Greeks. The secret of the horse, he told them, was that it would bring certain victory to whoever possessed it.

When the people of Troy heard this, it made them very eager to have it for their own. They made up their minds that they would take the horse into the city in spite of the Greeks. Tremendous ropes were made and tied to the horse. Hundreds of Trojan citizens gathered around and pulled and tugged and pushed and sweated until at last the horse stood inside the city walls.

Then the Trojans held a great feast. They rejoiced that they had finally been set free from the Greeks and that the war was now over. All day long the Trojans, soldiers and civilians alike, ate and drank. When night came, most of them were so full of food and wine that they lay down wherever they were and fell fast asleep. They forgot all about the dangers of the last nine years of war. Even the guards were drowsing at their posts.

Then when all was quiet in the sleeping city, the

*Silently, they lowered ladders . . . climbed down,
rushed to the city gates, and threw them wide open.*

Greek soldiers inside the wooden horse swung open the concealed doors. Silently, they lowered ladders. Then they climbed down, rushed to the city gates, and threw them wide open.

Thousands of Greek soldiers from the ships which had returned during the night lay in waiting. The invaders poured in through the opened gates to join their comrades in arms. Then, the attack began!

The Trojans, taken completely by surprise, were overcome. Troy was laid waste. King Menelaus rescued his kidnapped queen, and the beautiful Helen sailed back with her husband to Sparta.

So it was, that whereas all the strength of the Greeks could not overcome Troy, the foolish curiosity of the Trojans themselves proved to be their undoing.

THE GOLDEN FLEECE

The Voyage of the Argonauts

OLD KING AESON of Thessaly was worn and weary
with the heavy cares of governing his people. He
longed to have his handsome little son, Jason, take
his place on the throne. But Jason was young, much
too young to rule over a kingdom. Yet the king was
too old and too tired to go on.

So Aeson called his brother, Pelias, before him and
said: "My brother, I can no longer rule. While my
little son, Jason, is still a child, I would have you take
the throne in my place. But you must agree that when
Jason reaches manhood, he, the rightful ruler, shall
be king."

Pelias readily agreed. But secretly he made up his mind that Jason would never be seated upon the throne of Thessaly. To find out just how he might keep the kingdom for himself, Pelias went to an oracle. The oracles were fortune tellers. In those days, people believed that an oracle had the mystic power to see into the future.

After mumbling a few charms and burning some magic powders, the oracle told Pelias, "Fear not anyone who cometh not with and without a shoe!"

This strange reply satisfied Pelias that he had nothing to fear from Jason. But to make doubly sure that Jason would never cause him trouble, after the old King Aeson died, Pelias banished Jason to a faraway land, many weeks' journey from Thessaly.

There in that far-off country, Jason was reared. He grew into boyhood; and when it came time for Jason to go to school, he was sent to study with the Centaurs.

A centaur was a strange creature, half man and half horse. Below the waist, the centaur had the four legs and body of a horse, which gave him the speed and strength of that animal. From the waist up, the centaur was a man, gifted with the intelligence of men. The centaurs were famous for being very learned. In addition they were known for their tremendous bravery and skill as fighters and archers.

Young Jason's special teacher was Chiron, the chief of the centaurs. Chiron was delighted with Jason's wit and quickness. Chiron taught so well, and Jason learned so readily, that soon the youth was a master of the manly arts, and had a goodly store of the world's wisdom.

Jason did not know that he was a king's son. But when the young prince reached manhood, Chiron the centaur, satisfied that Jason was fit to be a king, told him the story of his royal birth. Jason determined to win his throne back from his wicked uncle, Pelias.

So Chiron consulted an oracle for advice on how Jason should overcome his uncle. Again came a strange reply:

"Whoever seeketh the crown shall wear a leopard's hide!" said the oracle.

Heeding the oracle's words, Jason ventured deep into the forest and killed a leopard. Then Jason dressed himself in the leopard's skin. He said farewell to Chiron, and set forth on his way to Thessaly.

Soon Jason came to a rushing river. The stream was so wide and rough, and its current so strong, that the people who stood on the river bank warned Jason not to try to cross. Many men had tried, the people said, but no man had been able to cross the river alive.

Undaunted, Jason stepped into the raging current. The swirling waters pulled angrily at the young man who dared defy its power. The trunks of huge trees, being carried down the stream, rushed at Jason like mad things. One slip—one moment of carelessness—

. . . Chiron consulted an oracle for advice on how Jason should overcome his wicked uncle.

and Jason would go down, never to be seen again. Step by step he made his way across, while those who watched from the river's banks held their breath. There were only three steps, two steps, one step more to go—when suddenly the watchers saw Jason swept off his feet!

A groan went up from the many lips. The brave young man who had braved the torrent was lost! But no! One powerful arm reached up and grasped a large branch of a tree which overhung the river. Slowly Jason pulled himself to safety on the far bank of the river. He had won his first great test!

Jason rested but a moment. When he stood up, he suddenly realized that one of his feet was bare.

Slowly Jason pulled himself to safety . . .

He had lost one of his sandals in the rushing river. But eager to reach Thessaly, he strode forward.

It was not long before Jason came to his own city. As he walked through the streets of Thessaly, clad only in a leopard skin and one sandal, a great commotion arose. People, seeing this handsome youth, remembered the old prophecy that a young man would appear, wearing only one sandal, and that he would be their rightful king.

The false king pretended that he was glad to see Jason. Pelias said he had only been holding Jason's kingdom for him until his return and that he would be glad to turn the throne over to the Prince.

Then Pelias beguiled Jason with a royal feast of welcome. With his nephew in fine humor, Pelias craftily told Jason of a glorious adventure which would make the youth famous all over the world. "Far away, in the land of Colchis, there is a Golden Fleece," he said. "This fleece is the skin of a golden sheep which is the rightful property of your family. But the Golden Fleece is held by the King of Colchis. It is guarded by a dragon which never sleeps. If I were a young man, nothing would stop me from winning the Golden Fleece."

When Jason heard this story, he was determined to win fame and glory by capturing the Golden Fleece. This was just as Pelias planned, for he was sure Jason would be killed on this dangerous quest.

Jason issued a call for brave men to accompany him on his adventure. From all parts of Greece they came. Jason chose only the bravest and the best. Soon there were assembled in Thessaly fifty of the greatest heroes of Greece.

Jason commissioned Argus to build him a ship . . . the like of which had never been seen before.

Jason commissioned Argus, a famous boatbuilder, to build him a ship, large enough to hold fifty men. Argus built a vessel, the like of which had never been seen before. It was strong and large.

When their ship was finished, the heroes called it the *Argo,* after Argus, the builder; and they themselves were called the Argonauts. Thus equipped, the fifty heroes set forth from Thessaly with Jason at their head. Good fortune seemed to favor them, for when the Argonauts came to Thrace, they were forewarned by Phineus, the sage, of a great danger which lay before them.

In the sea over which they had to sail were two rocky islands between which they must pass. But whenever anything passed between these islands, they would come crashing together with such speed that anything caught between the two islands was crushed to splinters.

"To avoid this terrible catastrophe," said Phineus, "when you approach the islands, let loose a dove. The dove, flying between the islands will cause them to rush together, but she can fly through swiftly enough to escape destruction. Then, at the moment when the islands start returning to their former places, you and your men lay to the oars, and row with all your might. With the help of the gods you may be fast enough to get through before the islands rush together again."

Jason and his companions thanked Phineus and continued on their way. Soon they came to the islands. The Argonauts drew as near to the fearful passage as possible. Then they released the dove. Straight as an arrow the bird flew between the islands. A roaring sound filled their ears as the islands came rushing together with a crash. But the dove was safe; only her tail feathers were caught between the rocky walls.

Jason's men sat alertly at the oars, ready at Jason's signal to row with all their strength. The moment the islands had separated enough for the *Argo* to sail through, Jason gave the signal. Then, as one man, the Argonauts plied their oars. As they pulled, the sweat stood out on every oarsman's brow.

Swift as a bird the *Argo,* with its crew of heroes, sped between the islands. The islands separated their full distance, and then with fearful speed, came crashing together again. By just the breadth of a hair, the *Argo* slipped through. Actually, the tip of the dreadful islands grazed the stern of the boat.

At last the heroes came to the kingdom of Colchis. Jason made known to the king his determination to get the Golden Fleece. The king laughed.

"O ho, you think that all you have to do is come here and demand the Golden Fleece and it is yours! Not so fast, my young fellow. Do you not know that the first thing you must do is to harness the fire-breathing bulls? Then you must plow the stony field which lies next to the temple of Mars. After that you must sow the dragon's teeth in the field. Then we shall see what happens."

But Jason was not frightened or discouraged. "Let us not delay a moment," he cried. "Lead us to our tasks!"

So the king led Jason and his companions to the field of the bulls. The fierce red eyes of the bulls

glared angrily at Jason and his bold crew. As the
bulls pawed the ground, the fiery breath which curled
from their nostrils, scorched the ground for many
yards around them. No man could get close enough
to harness the ferocious beasts without being burned
to a crisp by the flames they breathed out. The Argonauts were forced to withdraw from the field.

That night, in the Argonauts' encampment, Jason
was in despair. Suddenly there stood before him a
maiden. It was the king's daughter, Medea. She had
fallen in love with Jason.

"Do not be downhearted," she said. "No mortal
man, unaided, could have overcome these enchanted
bulls. But I can help you. If you promise to marry
me and carry me off with you, I will help you to win

*A roaring sound filled their ears as the islands
came rushing together with a crash.*

the Golden Fleece." Jason agreed.

Then she gave him a magic herb. "This will tame the bulls," she said.

Next, she gave him a heavy black stone, saying, "Use this when the need arises."

At dawn, the next morning, Jason went into the field alone. When the bulls came stamping toward him, he held out the magic herb and lo! the bulls became tame! They crouched gently at Jason's feet and permitted him to yoke them to the plow.

When the king and his court arose, there was Jason, quietly plowing the field of Mars with the now gentle bulls.

The king was furious, and suspected treachery, but not for one moment did he suspect his own daughter.

"Here," he said, "in this warrior's helmet are the dragon's teeth. Sow them in the field you have plowed."

Jason took the helmet and did as he was bid. No sooner had he strewed the seeds in the furrows than little shiny points began to appear. As Jason watched, the points grew. Soon, to his horror, he saw a most remarkable thing. Each of the teeth which he had sown was becoming an armed warrior. First their spears appeared, then their helmets and, right under his eyes, Jason saw an army of soldiers come up out of the ground. No sooner had they sprouted, than the soldiers brandished their spears and rushed upon him.

Jason drew his sword to fight, but how could one man hope to win against so many?

Then he remembered the weapon Medea had given him. The stone. That was it! Now must be the time to use it!

Quick as a flash, Jason threw the stone right into the midst of the army. The man who was hit, sure that his neighbor had struck him, turned angrily and struck him back. In a matter of moments, the thousand soldiers who had sprung from the dragon's teeth were fighting each other. They fought each other, instead of Jason, until not one of the army was left alive.

Now the king's daughter quickly drew near to Jason.

"Quick!" whispered Medea. "To the fleece!"

She handed Jason a magic potion.

Jason rushed to the garden where the fleece, guarded by the dragon who never slept, was hanging on a tree.

Jason sprinkled a few drops of the potion before the dragon, and its hideous head rolled from side to side as it fell into a deep sleep. Then Jason drew his sword and cut off the dragon's head. He looked about him and there hanging on the limb of a tree, was the Golden Fleece. It gleamed like the sun. Jason seized the precious prize and shouted to his comrades to follow him to their ship. Medea, too, made for the ship, for she well knew what her fate would be

*Then Jason drew his sword and cut off the
dragon's head.*

when her father discovered her part in helping Jason
—as he surely would.

In a rage, the king gathered together his men and
pursued his daughter and the Argonauts, hoping to
catch them before they reached their ship. But the
Argonauts were too swift and too strong for the king's
men, and they made good their escape.

The *Argo,* with its dauntless crew, had many peri-
lous moments on the return voyage, but with the
help of the gods, who applauded their bravery, they
at last reached Thessaly again.

Now, with the help of fifty heroes, Jason forced
the evil King Pelias to yield the kingdom to him, its
rightful ruler.

THE STORY OF THESEUS

Young Liberator of a Kingdom

IN THE KINGDOM of Athens there once lived a good king named Aegeus. He journeyed many miles from Athens to a faraway land where he married the beautiful Princess Aethra.

Alas! Before the time came for King Aegeus to return to Athens with his lovely queen, a messenger arrived bearing terrible news. The kingdom of Athens had been attacked by the armies of King Minos of Crete!

With sorrow in his heart, King Aegeus knew he must leave his bride behind in her father's kingdom. Before he bade her farewell, however, he led her to the top of a hill, on which there lay a mighty stone.

"I can stay no longer, dear wife," he said. "The child you will bear in a short time, I cannot see. I know not how long this war will last, or how long it will be before I can come for you. But see, under this stone I have placed a sword and a pair of sandals. When our son is strong enough to lift this stone and take the sword and sandals for himself, let him come to me in Athens."

Then Aegeus kissed his wife and set forth for the besieged land of Athens.

Soon a son was born to Queen Aethra. She named him Theseus. The young prince was brought up as befitted a king's son in those warlike days. He was taught to ride the most spirited horses, taught to shoot an arrow straight and true, and taught to handle a sword with skill and daring. Soon there were none more proficient in the arts of war than Theseus.

The years passed swiftly, but Aegeus did not return for his queen, and she could not know what misfortune had befallen him, or his kingdom of Athens. But with the years, the young prince Theseus grew in beauty and courage and strength.

Queen Aethra heeded her husband's instructions. There came a day when she felt it was time to test the strength of their son, Prince Theseus. On that day, mother and son walked up the hill to the place where King Aegeus had hidden the sword and sandals.

"My son," said she, "Can you lift this stone?"

Without a word, the young man leaned down. With astonishing ease Theseus lifted the enormous stone, and looked wonderingly at the jewel-encrusted sword and handsome gold sandals that lay underneath.

"Ah, my son, the time has come for us to part! Now you are a man. You have just proven that. And as a man, you must go to your father, my husband, Aegeus, the King of Athens. The way is long and dangerous, but you have strength, and youth, and courage. May good fortune follow you."

So saying, his mother bade him farewell. Then Theseus kissed her fondly and set out for his father's kingdom.

The first day's journey brought Theseus into the land where dwelled Epidaurus, the robber giant. Epidaurus the Club-carrier, he was called, for in his hand he always carried an immense iron club. Many an innocent wayfarer had been waylaid and beaten to death by this wicked giant.

From afar, Epidaurus spied the handsome young Theseus as he swung cheerfully along the highroad.

"O ho!" chortled the robber, "here's a rich prize! An elegant young nobleman he must be, for look at his fine clothes. It will be a moment's work to club this namby-pamby lad and pocket his gold. I'll hide behind this clump of trees, and boff! That will be the end of him!"

But Theseus was no fool. Warily he approached the clump of trees, keeping his ears alert for any suspicious sound. Epidaurus sprang! But Theseus was ready for him. Nimbly dodging the blow of the fearful iron club, Theseus stretched out his foot and sent the clumsy giant sprawling. The club flashed past Theseus' head, and with a mighty thud buried itself harmlessly in the ground. The giant reached over to retrieve the club.

Quick as a wink Theseus leaped on Epidaurus. Before the robber could regain his balance, Theseus wrenched the club from his powerful hands. Again the giant lunged, and again Theseus side-stepped. Now the young prince, his muscles straining, lifted the giant's club. The tip flashed in the sunlight as Theseus lifted it over his head. Then, crash! Try as he might, the robber giant could not escape that mighty blow. It landed fair on the robber's brow, and with a groan he sank to earth, and breathed his last. No longer would Epidaurus terrorize innocent travelers!

Athens was not many days' journey away, when Theseus met up with the terrible man called Procrustes the Stretcher. Procrustes had a house in a lonely spot along the road. When a footsore traveler passed that way, Procrustes would welcome him cunningly, with false smiles and deceiving words. He would offer the weary wayfarer food and drink and rest. But no one ever left Procrustes' dreadful house alive.

In the house Procrustes had an iron bed which, he boasted, would exactly fit anyone who lay on it. Sure enough it did. For no sooner had the traveler fallen asleep on the bed, when iron arms came down and clamped him in place. Then if the stranger were longer than the bed, Procrustes would chop off his limbs; if he were shorter than the bed, the pitiless monster would stretch the traveler's limbs to fit the length.

But Procrustes met his match in Theseus. When Procrustes led Theseus to the terrible iron bed, the young prince pretended he did not know how to lie in it. The wicked Procrustes lay down on the bed himself to show Theseus what to do. Whereupon Theseus leaped on Procrustes, and taking him by surprise, tied his arms and legs to the bed. Then Theseus treated Procrustes exactly as Procrustes had treated so many others.

And so, Theseus set forth upon his journey again. When at last the city of Athens loomed ahead, Theseus sped on with joy in his heart. He did not know that his most dangerous adventure still lay ahead of him.

In Athens, where Theseus expected to find only joy at his arrival, he found instead sadness. Of course King Aegeus was happy to see his stalwart son, but in his heart there was a great sorrow for his kingdom and his people.

"You have come at a sad and troublous time," the

. . . *Theseus stretched out his foot and sent the clumsy giant sprawling.*

king told Theseus. "I must tell you that Athens was conquered in war by King Minos of Crete. And now we must pay him a terrible price. Every year we must send seven of our noblest youths and seven of our loveliest maidens to the Island of Crete to be devoured by the Minotaur."

When Theseus heard this he cried, "My father, choose me to be one of the seven youths. I will go to Crete and slay the Minotaur."

"Oh, no, my son! You are the hope of Athens. You must become king when I die. Do not ask me to send you to your death!"

But Theseus answered, "Athens will die if its courage dies. I will go."

So in spite of his father's pleas, Theseus made ready to sail. The dread day of departure came, and the ship with its gloomy black sail was ready to lift anchor.

As Theseus said farewell to his father, he said, "This ship will surely return with everyone safe, believe it. And when we do, we shall change the black sail for a white sail. In that way you will know the good news from afar off, and you will rejoice."

"I shall be praying and watching," said King Aegeus.

In Crete, as the Athenian youths and maidens were marched through the streets to their prison, many people lined the way to look at them. There were many who were sorry for them when they saw how young they were.

Not so King Minos. He gloated over his triumph, and said to his lovely daughter Ariadne, who was standing with him, "See, this is the way I make sure that the Kingdom of Athens will never be strong again. The Minotaur will destroy their strongest and best while they are still young. They will never have a leader."

But the young princess felt pity for them in her heart. "They are too young and too noble to die," she mourned.

Then her eyes rested on the young hero, Theseus, and straightway she fell in love with him. She could not bear the thought that this tall young man, who stood like a king, should be devoured by the vile Minotaur. She must find a way to help him.

That night the door of Theseus' prison cell creaked open. A beautiful girl stepped into the room.

Theseus rose in wonder. "Fair maiden, who are you?" he asked, "and why have you come to my cell?"

"I am Ariadne, the daughter of the king," she answered, "and I have come to help you."

Then she handed him a sword and a ball of silken thread.

"The sword is for you to kill the ferocious Minotaur. The thread is your means of escape. Of what use would it be for you to kill the Minotaur and then

. . . the door of Theseus' prison cell creaked open.
A beautiful girl handed him a sword and
ball of silken thread.

die of hunger as you tried in vain to find your way out
of the labyrinth? But if you tie one end of the strong
thread to the doorpost of the labyrinth and unwind it
as you make your way through the passages to find
the beast, you will have a silken clue which will lead
you out again in safety."

"Why have you done this?" asked Theseus. "Why
do you help me?"

"Can you not tell?" said Ariadne.

"Beautiful princess, if I did not love you for your
beauty, I would love you for your goodness. I will
slay the Minotaur. See that my ship is ready. Wait for
me at the door of the labyrinth. I will take you with
me to Athens and make you my wife."

Ariadne hastened away, with her heart full of hope.
The next day, Theseus and his companions were led
into the labyrinth. Theseus hid the sword and the ball
of thread under his cloak. He did as Ariadne had told
him, and tied one end of the thread to the doorpost.
Then he stepped boldly into the labyrinth and waited.

At last, they heard a distant sound of bellowing.
Their hearts froze within them.

"He is coming!" shouted Theseus. He drew his
sword.

Around the end of the passage came the Minotaur.
He was twice as tall as a man and he had the head of
a monstrous bull. He roared and rushed at the frightened Athenians. But when the Minotaur saw that The-

seus, instead of running away, was actually advancing to meet him, he reared back for a moment. No one had ever defied the terrible beast before. Then the Minotaur lowered his head, and with a terrifying bellow, he charged.

Theseus leaped aside, thrusting at the monster with his sword as he leaped. The savage blow cut off the leg of the Minotaur; and as the beast, bellowing and rolling about in his pain, tried to charge into Theseus with his sharp horns, Theseus pierced him through his

. . the Minotaur . . . with a terrifying bellow . . . charged.

heart. With an earth-shaking shudder, the Minotaur fell back dead.

Then the youths and maidens fell on their knees before Theseus. They kissed his hands in gratitude and swore eternal love to him for their rescue.

It was now almost night. Theseus, bidding the others follow him, wound the ball of thread as it led him through the endless corridors. At last they were at the gate and there stood Ariadne, with her arms outstretched in joy.

Under the cover of night, they made their way to the ship, and set sail for home with all possible speed.

Waiting in Athens, King Aegeus watched for their ship. Would it come back with black sails, telling of the death of his son and the others? Or would the ship have white sails, bearing a joyous message that all was well?

At last the vessel came into the harbor. But in the rejoicing that took place aboard the ship, they had forgotten to change the sail!

"Alas," cried Aegeus, "my son is dead! What joy is there left for me in this world?" And with that Aegeus flung himself into the sea and was drowned. And from that day on, even until the present day, that sea is called the Aegean Sea.

So Theseus became King of Athens, and ruled wisely and well.

DAEDALUS AND ICARUS

The Men Who Flew Like Birds

ON THE ISLAND of Crete, during the reign of King Minos, there lived a most skillful artisan named Daedalus. Daedalus was the greatest inventor and craftsman of his time, and his fame spread to the far corners of the world.

It was Daedalus who built the famous labyrinth in which King Minos kept that terrible beast, the Minotaur. This labyrinth was a building with hundreds of winding halls and passages, so complicated that no one who went into it could ever find his way out again.

But although Daedalus performed great services for King Minos, the king feared him. King Minos was afraid that Daedalus with his great wisdom and skill, might some day gain the throne of Crete. So the king caused Daedalus and his young son, Icarus, to be imprisoned in a dark, stone tower.

But no locks could hold Daedalus. For he could open them all! And one dark night Daedalus and young Icarus escaped from the tower.

After they had fled, Daedalus and Icarus did not find it so easy to escape from Crete. You see, Crete is an island, and King Minos had his soldiers search every ship that left its shores.

Daedalus and Icarus lay in hiding in a cave along the seashore. One bright day, Daedalus was idly watching the sea gulls soaring and swooping over the water in their search for food. Suddenly an idea struck him.

"King Minos may control the land and the sea," he cried, "but he does not control the air. That is how Icarus and I shall escape."

Then Daedalus set to work to study the birds and learn the secret of their flight. For endless hours he watched the birds flying. He caught a bird and studied the clever structure of its wings. Then he put to use his knowledge and skill to copy the wings of a bird. The boy, Icarus, spent his days trapping the sea gulls and plucking their feathers. Daedalus took the feathers which his son had obtained, and sewed them together with marvelous skill. Soon wings began to take shape, so wonderfully made that, except for their great size, they looked exactly like the wings of a real bird. And then Daedalus took these wings, and with melted wax attached them to a wooden framework.

When he had made a pair of wings for himself and a pair of wings for his son, Daedalus fastened them in place. A wing was strapped to each arm. Then Daedalus proceeded to teach his son to fly, just as a mother bird teaches her young. How happy and excited young Icarus was when he found that he could fly through the air, that he could circle and float on the wind! He was impatient to be off.

Finally the time came when Daedalus felt they were ready to make the escape from Crete. He turned to his son and said, "Icarus, listen carefully to my words. Follow close behind me in your flight. Do not fly too low or the dampness from the sea will cling to your wings and make them too heavy for you to lift. Do not fly too high or the sun will melt the wax of your wings."

Then Daedalus kissed his son fondly and began to rise into the air. Icarus followed his father. As the two of them flew across the sky, people looked up in amazement. The plowmen in the fields gazed upward, the shepherds marveled! They thought they were watching the flight of gods.

At first, Icarus stayed close behind his father. But then, exulting in his new-found power, he flew off

*As the two of them flew across the sky, people
looked up in amazement.*

on little side trips. Soon he forgot everything his
father had told him and flew high into the heavens.

Then the blazing sun did its work and the wax of
his wings melted. Icarus fluttered his arms, but there
were not enough feathers left to beat the air. He called
his father, but in vain. Down he fell into the sea!

Daedalus sped to the aid of his son, but when he
saw the feathers floating on the ocean, he knew to
his grief that Icarus had been drowned. So ended
man's first attempt to fly; for Daedalus, heart-broken
at the loss of his son, flew on to Sicily, took off his
wings and never flew again.

PANDORA'S BOX

The Gift of the Gods

WHEN THE EARTH was new, the gods on Mount Olympus decided to make a perfect creature and send their handiwork down to earth to grace and adorn the new world of men.

They made a beautiful woman in heaven, and they named her Pandora, meaning all-gifted, for all the gods and goddesses had contributed something to her making. Venus gave her beauty, Mercury gave her the art of persuasion, Apollo gave her the gift of music—each of them gave Pandora that gift which was the most precious thing in his power to bestow.

And then the gods sent Pandora to earth. As a

farewell offering, they gave her a beautiful box. They
warned Pandora that under no circumstances was she
to open it.

For a while Pandora was content. Why should she
not be? Everyone loved her. But Pandora, with all
her great talents, was not a goddess. She was just a
human being—like all of us. She wondered and wondered about what was in the beautiful box. Her curiosity grew stronger and stronger, and she longed to
know what was inside that box.

Finally, Pandora said to herself, "Who will ever
know if I take one little peek into the box. I won't
take anything out of it. I'll just open it a crack and
close it right up again. What harm can there be in
that?"

So Pandora, like most other human beings, gave in
to her curiosity and she disobeyed the gods. She took
the box and lifted the lid, ever so slightly. Suddenly,
she heard a whirring noise, and before she could do
anything, hundreds of horrible little creatures came
flying out of the box.

As quickly as she could Pandora clamped down
the lid again. But it was too late! In that brief moment, Pandora had released from the box all the evils
and sorrows of the world. A moment before, there
had been no Sickness or Grief; no Envy or Cruelty—
none of the things that mankind suffers today.

However, Pandora managed to close the fateful

. . . she heard a whirring noise and hundreds of
horrible little creatures came flying out of the box.

box before one last thing succeeded in escaping. That one thing was Hope.

Pandora heard the last creature which had been shut up in the box crying to be let out. So she lifted the lid again and released Hope. Out flew Hope and went all over the Earth helping everyone who was sad and lonely, and making everyone more cheerful by giving them part of herself—Hope.

So even though Pandora's mischievous curiosity brought to this earth all the sorrow and pain that fills the world, she also released Hope. And, thanks to Pandora, we shall always have Hope, that most wonderful of all good things.

THE GOLDEN TOUCH

The King Who Worshipped Gold

ONCE THERE DWELLED in the kingdom of Phrygia, a king called Midas. On the whole he was a good king, but he had one great fault. He loved riches more than anything else in the world. He loved gold not for the good he could do with it, but for the sake of the precious metal itself. The more gold the foolish man had, the more he wanted.

But in spite of his greed for gold, King Midas was at heart a kind man. When a weary old traveler who had lost his way knocked on the great golden doors of the king's palace, Midas gave the stranger food and drink, and a place to rest his head until he was sufficiently refreshed to continue his journey.

Shortly afterward, Midas was in his treasure room admiring his stacks of gold coins and his chests filled with precious jewels. Suddenly he sensed that there was someone in the room with him.

Who could it be? As usual all the doors to the treasure room were triple-locked, and King Midas had given strict orders that no one was to be permitted in the treasure chamber.

The King looked up. The stranger in the room with him was no ordinary mortal. Midas recognized him as the God Bacchus, come down from Mount Olympus.

The king was astonished. Imagine seeing one of the gods in his counting room!

Bacchus spoke. "Midas," he said, "you have shown great kindness to a weary stranger who came to your door. The stranger you befriended was Silenus, my foster-father. The gods do not forget such kindnesses. What is your fondest wish? Ask, and it shall be granted!"

Midas could hardly believe his good fortune. "Gold, gold!" he thought to himself. "I shall ask for gold. More gold than any mortal man has ever seen!"

Then the king spoke, "Oh, Bacchus, my lord, grant that anything I touch shall turn to gold!"

"You have made a poor choice," said Bacchus, "but if that is what you want, I must keep my promise and grant you your wish."

King Midas was overjoyed. Poor choice, Bacchus had said. Poor choice! Nonsense! How could anything to do with gold be poor? Midas rushed out into his garden. He must see if it was really true—if he really had the golden touch.

He snapped a twig from a tree and laughed with glee as he saw it turn to gold in his hand. He plucked an apple from a bough. Oh, joy! In his hand he held a perfect golden apple!

He rushed into his palace and ran from chair to chair. At his touch, they turned to gold. His excitement knew no bounds.

He sat down to the table, laden with delectable foods and wines. He raised a morsel of food to his mouth and took a bite. His teeth grated on something hard as stone. What was the matter? Taking the hard

He plucked an apple from a bough. Oh joy! In his hand he held a perfect golden apple!

substance from his mouth, he saw that it was a piece of gold.

In sudden fear, he plucked a luscious grape from a platter. In horror, he saw that its lush purple ripeness had changed to hard glittering gold. His heart was filled with terror because he knew he must starve to death if he could not be rid of the golden touch. Because he was so frightened, his mouth became dry with fear. He poured water into his wine to parch his thirst, but when he raised the goblet to his lips, he dashed it to the ground with dismay for molten gold had flowed into his mouth. The gold quickly hardened, and he spat it out in disgust.

Now he realized what Bacchus meant when he had said, "You have made a poor choice."

Poor indeed was Midas! Of what use was all his gold? Too late he realized that many things other than gold are precious. "How foolish I have been!" he cried.

Humbly, Midas prayed to Bacchus to take back the hated gift. The god took pity on him.

"Go to the River Pactolus and plunge into its waters," Bacchus told him. "Thus you shall be cleansed of the golden touch. Perhaps you will also be cleansed of your greed."

Midas quickly did as he was told and came out of the stream a changed man. To his joy, he had lost golden touch. But the gold had passed from his body to the sands of the River Pactolus and, even to this day, the sands still sparkle with gold.

Because King Midas had been cured of his greed for gold, he no longer wanted to look at his treasures; so he wandered into the woods and meadows and there he worshipped the god, Pan.

Pan was the god of all the forests and pastures and their wild life. He was an ugly but merry little man— with pointed ears and horns and legs like a goat's. Pan spent much of his carefree life playing on the pipes he had made from reeds growing by the river.

Pan's music was quite rough but it was jolly and gay and the wood nymphs and the creatures of the forest all loved it—and so did Midas. Pan, too, loved his own music but he grew vain about his powers and boasted that his skill was as great as that of Apollo, the great Sun God and the Lord of Music.

Now Midas was still a very foolish man in spite of the painful lesson he had learned about gold. He continued to praise Pan after he had made his boast and assured him that his music was even greater than that of Apollo.

A contest between Apollo and Pan was arranged. When the two had finished playing there was no doubt at all that Apollo was still the great Lord of Music. There was only one person who did not agree. That one was Midas. He continued to protest that Pan's music was greater than the noble music of

*Then Midas felt that his ears were growing
long and furry.*

Apollo, in spite of the outcome of the contest.

This made Apollo very angry. He looked at Midas sternly and said, "You have made poor use of your ears. You are unworthy to have human ears."

Then Midas felt that his ears were growing long and furry. They had changed to the ears of an ass. In all other ways Midas remained a human being, but he now had ass' ears.

Of course, Midas was terribly ashamed of his ears and had them covered up by a purple turban, which he always wore. But one of his servants had seen the ass' ears before they were covered. He knew he would be severely punished by King Midas if he told anyone but he could not bear to keep the secret to himself.

At last the servant could contain himself no longer. He went out into the middle of a meadow and dug a hole in the ground and put his mouth to it. Then he whispered into the hole, "Sh-sh-sh! Midas has ass' ears. Sh-sh-sh! Midas has ass' ears. Sh!"

Then he carefully covered over the hole and went away, happy to be relieved of his secret, but pleased to have told no one.

Time passed and a crop of reeds grew up from the hole. When they grew tall the reeds whispered in the wind, "Sh-sh-sh! Midas has ass' ears. Sh-sh-sh! Midas has ass' ears. Sh-sh-sh!" And soon everyone knew the king's secret.

THE GORDIAN KNOT

The Destiny of Alexander

MANY, MANY HUNDREDS of years ago, there lay in the western part of Asia a sleepy little kingdom named Phrygia. Far off the beaten track, Phrygia was neither important for its commerce nor for its culture nor for its military might. Nevertheless, the tiny kingdom had become famous throughout the world.

Phrygia's fame rested on a humble wagon that stood in the Temple of Jupiter. This wagon had been made fast to a wooden yoke with such a marvelous knot that, for over a hundred years, no one had been able to untie it. It was called the Gordian Knot because it had been tied by Gordius, the very first ruler of the Kingdom of Phrygia.

The oracles of the temple—those priests who were believed to have the power to foresee the future—had made a fateful prophecy:

*Whosoever undoes this wonderful work
shall have the world for his kingdom*

This promise had attracted many kings and princes and warriors to Phrygia. Each, hoping he might be the one to succeed and would then have the world for his kingdom, tried to untie the knot. But in the thousands of attempts made in a full hundred years, no one had even been able to unravel a single cord.

One day, word came that young King Alexander of Macedonia was coming to visit Phrygia. Although he was only twenty-three years old, Alexander had already conquered all of Greece and his fame had spread far and wide. Alexander was coming to grapple with the famous Gordian Knot.

On the fateful day, excitement was unbounded. A huge crowd filled the courtyard of the Temple of Jupiter. Young Alexander, surrounded by the notables of the city, approached the wagon.

"Is this the wondrous Gordian Knot?" he asked.

"The oracles have prophesied," said the elders of Phrygia, "that the man who should undo this knot would have the whole world for his kingdom."

Alexander studied the knot carefully. Then without

. . . he drew his sword from its scabbard, and brought it down with one mighty stroke . . .

a word, he drew his sword from its scabbard, and rais-
ing it above his head, brought it down with one
mighty stroke and cut the Gordian Knot in two.

"It is thus," cried Alexander, "that I unravel all
Gordian Knots!"

Alexander went on to fulfill the old prophecy.
With his victorious armies he conquered nearly all of
the known world.

And then, the story goes, Alexander, who had succeeded in gaining the whole world for his kingdom,
sat down and wept, for there were no new worlds for
him to conquer.

ECHO AND NARCISSUS

The Nymph and the Vain Youth

IN ANCIENT TIMES, lovely enchanted creatures called nymphs lived in the fields and the forests. They made their homes in the trees and in the flowers and in the streams. Their food was fairy food.

Echo was one of these charming creatures. She was lovely to look at as she flitted about the forests. She could have been a perfect delight to her companions —except for one thing. Echo talked too much! Not only that, but she insisted on having the last word in every conversation.

This annoying habit finally so angered Juno, the queen of the gods, that she decided to punish Echo.

"This shall be your punishment," Juno said. "You shall no longer be able to talk—with this exception: you have always insisted on having the last word; so, Echo, now you will never be able to say anything, you will only be able to repeat *the last word!*"

Now in the forest where the nymphs dwelt, a handsome young man named Narcissus used to go hunting. So handsome was he, even the lovely nymphs fell in love with him at first sight. But Narcissus was terribly vain. He felt that no one was good enough to deserve his love.

One day, Echo caught sight of Narcissus and straightway fell in love with him. She yearned to tell him of her love; but because of Juno's punishment, she was powerless to speak. Echo followed Narcissus adoringly wherever he went. But now that she could no longer speak, Echo became very shy.

One day, while out hunting, Narcissus became separated from his companions. Hearing a sound in the woods nearby, he called out "Who's there?"

It was Echo. But all she could answer was the last word "There!"

Narcissus called again. "Come!" he said.

"Come!" replied Echo.

Still seeing no one, Narcissus cried, "Why do you shun me?"

"Shun me!" came back the reply.

"Let us join each other," called Narcissus.

Then Echo, full of love, stepped out from between the trees.

"Each other!" she repeated, giving Narcissus both her hands.

But Narcissus drew back in his pride. "Go away," he said. "Do not touch me! I would rather die than that you should have me."

"Have me," wept Echo.

But in his cold pride Narcissus left her.

Echo was heartbroken. From then on, she pined away. Echo grew thinner and thinner. Finally, nothing was left of her—but her voice.

Echo still lives among the rocks and caves of the mountains where she answers anyone who calls her. But she answers with only the last word.

The heartless Narcissus was not to escape punishment. He continued in his vain self-love until one day he cruelly spurned another nymph who sought his affection. The hurt creature in her anguish entreated the Goddess of Love:

"Oh, Goddess," she prayed, "make this hardhearted young man know what it is to love someone who does not return his love. Let him feel the pain I now suffer."

The nymph's prayer was heard. In the middle of the forest, there was a clear fountain. Here Narcissus wandered one day, and bending over to drink, he caught sight of his own reflection in the water. He thought he saw a beautiful water nymph. Gazing in admiration, Narcissus fell in love with himself!

He stretched out his arms to clasp the beautiful being he saw in the water. The creature stretched out its arms, too. Narcissus plunged his arms into the water to embrace his beloved. Instantly, the water shivered into a thousand ripples and the creature disappeared.

A few moments later his beloved reappeared. Now Narcissus brought his lips near to the water to take a kiss. Again the image fled!

He begged his adored one to stay.

"Why do you shun me?" he cried. "I am not ugly. The nymphs love me. Even you look at me lovingly. When I stretch out my arms, you do the same. When I blow you kisses, you answer them."

His tears fell into the water and the image began to disappear.

"Stay, I implore you!" he begged. "If I may not touch you, at least let me look at you."

Narcissus would not leave the pool. Now he knew the pain of loving in vain. Gradually, he grew pale and faded away. As he pined in hopeless love, he lost his beauty.

The nymph, Echo, hovered near him and sorrowed for him. And when he murmured, "Alas, alas!" she answered, "Alas!"

Finally, he died of grief. The nymphs prepared to

Narcissus plunged his arms into the water to
embrace his beloved.

bury him. But when they came for him, he was no-where to be found. In his place, bending over the pool, they found a beautiful flower.

And to this day, this lovely flower grows near the water and is called the narcissus.

SWORD OF DAMOCLES
The Man Who Would Be King

THERE WAS ONCE a rich and powerful king in Greece named Dionysius. A clever, ruthless man, Dionysius had fought his way to the throne, winning out over many other claimants. But though he gained the crown, Dionysius had made many powerful and bitter enemies in his struggle for that prize. Yet there were many who envied Dionysius and wished they were in his place.

Amongst the king's courtiers was a man called Damocles. Damocles was constantly praising Dionysius and saying, "Oh great king, you are indeed blessed of the gods. Everything you could wish for is yours. How happy you must be!"

One day, when Damocles was speaking in his flattering way, Dionysius said, "How now, Damocles, what say you? Would you like to be king in my stead?"

Damocles was frightened, for he did not want the king to think that he was plotting to seize the throne. Quickly he replied, "Oh no, great king, I would not be king. I was only thinking how wonderful it would be to enjoy your riches for even one day."

"It shall be as you desire," said King Dionysius. "For one day, you shall enjoy the position and power and luxury of a king. You shall know exactly what it feels like to be in my place."

The next day the astonished Damocles was led into the king's chamber. He was dressed in royal robes and told that he could do whatever he wished.

He ordered delicious wines and food to be served to him. He commanded singers and dancers to amuse him, and he prepared to enjoy every luxury.

Suddenly, as he leaned back among his silken cushions, he gasped with horror. Just above his head was an enormous sword hanging by a slender thread! If the thread broke, the sword would fall and kill him.

He sat, pale and trembling. Pointing to the sword in terror, he whispered, "That sword! That sword! Why is that sword hanging above me? Hanging by so slender a thread?"

. . . pointing to the sword in terror, he whispered,
"Why is that sword hanging above me?"

"I promised you," answered Dionysius, "that you should know exactly how it feels to live like a king, and now you know! Did you expect that you might enjoy all of a king's riches for nothing? Do you not know that I always live with a sword hanging over my head? I must be on my guard every moment lest I be slain."

Then Damocles answered, "Oh King, take back your wealth and your power! I would not have it for another moment. I would rather be a poor peasant living in a mountain hut than live in fear and trembling all the days of my life!"

Never again did Damocles envy the king.

ATALANTA'S RACE

A Contest for Love or Death

ONE OF THE LOVELIEST maidens in the Greece of long ago was a girl named Atalanta. Many were the handsome suitors who sought her hand. But Atalanta was simply not interested in any of them, nor even in the idea of marriage.

The young men, however, were not easily discouraged. They constantly urged her to listen to their pleas.

Finally she hit upon a scheme to discourage her suitors. She gathered them all together and said, "Whoever wants to marry me must run a race with me. If he wins, I will marry him. But if he loses, he must pay for his loss with his life!"

Atalanta's strange proposal had the desired effect
with most of her young men. Besides her beauty, Atalanta was renowned throughout Greece for her prow-
ess in sports. It was said that she was the swiftest
runner in the world—that she could outrun anyone except Mercury, the fleet messenger of the gods.

But there still remained a few young men so smit-
ten with Atalanta that they were willing to gamble
their lives against such overwhelming odds. So a time
for the race was set.

Hippomenes, a young man who had never seen Atalanta, was chosen to be judge. When he learned the
conditions of the race, he was astounded. "How could
any girl be worth such a risk?" he wondered.

But on the day of the race, when Hippomenes saw
the fair Atalanta, he too fell in love with her!

The race began. Hippomenes watched, his heart
pounding with fear, lest one of the young men win
the race and carry off the beautiful prize. But they were
all far behind Atalanta as she flew across the finish
line. One and all, the young men had to pay with their
lives for their reckless ardor.

But Hippomenes, whose heart now was hopelessly
lost to Atalanta, was not daunted by the dreadful fate
of the others. He came to Atalanta and said, "Fair
maid, I would try for your hand."

Atalanta looked at him pityingly. How could she

let this handsome young man throw his life away?
She tried to discourage Hippomenes.

"You have seen what happened to the others," she
told him. "You see how fleet of foot I am. Do not
try to race against me. You will surely lose the race
and your life with it."

But Hippomenes would not be put off. He insisted
that Atalanta keep to her terms.

Hippomenes prayed to Venus, the Goddess of Love.
"Oh, Venus," he prayed, "whatever aid you can give
me, grant it now, for if I love Atalanta so deeply it
must be that you have willed it so."

Venus heard his prayer. Just as the race was about
to begin, three golden apples appeared in Hippomenes' hand. They could only have come from Venus'
own garden. As Hippomenes looked at the apples in
amazement, a soft voice whispered in his ear, "Race
well, Hippomenes. And if you have the wit to use
these golden apples correctly, they will win the race
for you."

Atalanta and Hippomenes moved to the starting
line. The watching crowds were impatient for the race
to begin. The signal was given and off they went.

At first Hippomenes, a very fine runner himself,
kept pace with Atalanta. But soon the maiden, darting forward as gracefully as a bird, began to draw
away from him.

The spectators were all hoping for Hippomenes to

win. "Faster! Faster!" they cried. But the young man's throat was dry—his stout heart felt as though it were going to burst within him. Try as he might, the maiden kept ahead of him, running easily.

Then Hippomenes remembered the gift of Venus. He threw one of the golden apples so that it landed near Atalanta's twinkling feet. Atalanta was entranced by it. "What is that beautiful shining thing?" she wondered. She stopped to pick up the beautiful, shining apple, and while she paused Hippomenes raced past her.

Atalanta was not alarmed. She knew that she could easily catch up to Hippomenes and go on past him. Besides, she was beginning to feel sorry for the handsome young man. "He is so young to die," she thought. "It is not because he is handsome and bold that I pity him; it is only because he is so young."

But Atalanta straightened up, and with the apple in her hand, sped after Hippomenes. In a moment she had caught up with him again, and in a few more strides she left him behind.

Again Hippomenes flung a golden apple ahead of Atalanta. The maiden stooped to scoop it up. Once again, Hippomenes raced past her. But it did not take long for Atalanta to close the distance between them and draw far ahead once more.

The winning post came into sight and the spectators held their breath. There seemed to be no hope

The maiden stooped to scoop it up. Once again,
Hippomenes raced past her.

for the brave young man.

Hippomenes' lungs seemed to be bursting within him. Gasping for breath, he sent up a prayer to Venus and he hurled the last apple. This time he tossed it off to one side. Atalanta, running after it, left the path to pursue the apple. Now Hippomenes made a final desperate effort. With a last burst of strength he threw himself forward and sped over the goal, a scant step ahead of the flying girl.

So with the help of Venus, Goddess of Love, Hippomenes won the lovely Atalanta. But Atalanta was very happy. She knew that though she had lost the race, she had won true love.

PROMETHEUS
The Giver of Fire

THE OLD GREEK LEGENDS tell us that first the gods made the earth. Then they gave the task of creating the creatures of the earth to two giants. One was named Prometheus, which means forethought, and the other was named Epimetheus, which means afterthought.

The giants were well named. Epimetheus gave special gifts to all the animals. He gave powerful wings to the eagle, great strength and courage to the lion, and cunning to the fox; but when it came time to provide for Man, he had nothing special left to give him. He had not thought of that in time.

Then Prometheus spoke: "Man should be superior to all living things on earth. How can we make him thus? We must give him a very special gift. But you and I have nothing left to give, so we must take our gift from the gods."

Then Prometheus went up to heaven, the home of the gods. There he crept into the palace of the Sun and stole a brand of fire which he brought back to earth. This was his gift to man.

And to Man he said, "With fire, you will be able to make weapons; and with weapons in your hands, you can overcome the fiercest and strongest animals.

"You will be able to build strong houses to shelter you from the weather, and fire will warm your homes for you and keep you alive in the bitterest cold.

"Fire shall make you the mightiest creature on earth!"

The gift was a great one, indeed.

But Prometheus paid a heavy price for his kindness in giving the gift of fire to Man. For Jupiter, the King of the Gods, was so enraged when he discovered that the gods' secret had been stolen, that he ordered Prometheus to be chained to a rock on the top of a mountain, in punishment for his deed.

There Prometheus was forced to lie, while vultures gnawed perpetually at his insides; for no matter how long the birds tore at his vitals, they never completely consumed them.

*. . . Jupiter, the King of the Gods . . . ordered
Prometheus chained to a rock . . .*

For hundreds of years, Prometheus lay bound like this, too proud to ask Jupiter for mercy, until Hercules, the hero who was half man and half god, broke Prometheus' chains and at last released him from his agony.

ARACHNE

The Story of the Spider

THE MAIDEN, ARACHNE, was so skillful at weaving and embroidery that people would come from far and near to marvel at her work.

Not only was the work itself beautiful, but Arachne's movements as she wove were so graceful and lovely that people would say, "Minerva herself must have taught you!"

But Arachne had become so conceited and vain of her skill that she could not bear to hear even the goddess Minerva praised.

"Let Minerva come," scoffed Arachne. "Let the great goddess herself try her skill against mine. If I do not surpass her, I will pay the penalty!"

Then Minerva, hearing this, was angry. But in her greatness she was still merciful. She disguised herself as an old woman and came to Arachne.

"I am an old woman," she said, "and I have learned much in my long lifetime. Challenge your fellow mortals, if you will, but do not challenge a goddess. If I were you, I would beg Minerva's forgiveness for your words, and pray that she will pardon you."

But Arachne laughed scornfully at the goddess in disguise.

"You are a stupid old woman," she said. "I am not afraid; I meant what I said. Let Minerva come down and compete with me, if she dares!"

"She comes!" answered Minerva; and dropping her disguise, she stepped forward.

Arachne paled, but only for a moment. "Let us begin," she replied.

The contest began. Minerva wove scenes showing the immense power of the gods. The beauty of her work was so great that the watchers were breathless with admiration.

Then Arachne began to weave. She purposely chose to weave pictures showing the weaknesses and errors of the gods. Her pictures were so lifelike they almost seemed to move. She wove so marvelously that even Minerva herself could not help but admire Arachne's art. But, furious at Arachne's insult, Minerva struck

. . . furious at Arachne's insult, Minerva struck
her shuttle, and it fell to pieces.

her shuttle, and it fell to pieces. Then she touched Arachne's forehead and made her feel her guilt and shame.

Arachne, in remorse, rushed away and hanged herself. Seeing this, Minerva took pity on her and said, "Live, guilty woman! But from now on you and all your children shall continue to hang."

As she spoke, Arachne's form shriveled up, while her arms and legs grew thinner, until finally she was changed into a spider.

And to this day, her descendants can be seen hanging from the thread which they weave into a web.

CIRCE

The Outwitting of an Enchantress

ONE OF THE longest and most terrible wars of ancient times was the nine years' war between the Greeks and the Trojans. In that war, the greatest of the Greek generals was, perhaps, King Ulysses of Ithaca. It was his clever strategy which finally resulted in the capture of Troy and victory for the Greek armies.

As Ulysses and his men were sailing for home, they ran short of supplies. When they came to a beautiful island, Ulysses landed and climbed a high hill. Spying a palace in the distance, Ulysses sent a party, under Eurylochus, to seek provisions there.

Eurylochus and the men approached the palace

cautiously. Suddenly, they found themselves surrounded by lions, tigers, wolves, and all sorts of fierce-
looking animals. They stood, transfixed with fear. But
the animals did not attack them. On the contrary, they
seemed completely tame and walked quietly amongst
the men.

The men did not know it, but they had wandered
into the kingdom of Circe, the enchantress. These
animals had once been men, but they had been
changed into beasts by Circe!

At that very moment, the men heard a lovely voice
singing. Not realizing the terrible danger they were
in, they pressed forward.

The singing stopped, and Circe, the beautiful but
wicked sorceress, came out to greet them. Sweetly, she
asked them to come in to rest and refresh themselves.
The men hurried forward, delighted with their welcome — all but Eurylochus, their wise leader. Something did not seem right to him. His suspicions were
aroused, and he did not enter the palace but stood
where he could look in and watch.

Circe ordered her servants to spread delicious food
before the men. Jars of wine were served to them. The
men ate and drank ravenously. That was just what
Circe wanted, for the food was enchanted. When Circe
saw that they had eaten and drunk their fill, she
touched each one with her wand.

Instantly, they were changed into swine. These

men, who, a moment before, were stalwart seamen, now had the snouts and ugly, bristly forms of pigs. They could not talk; they could only grunt. But their minds and feelings were still those of the men they had been.

Eurylochus, horrified at what he had seen, rushed back to the ship. He told Ulysses what had happened.

When Ulysses heard the fearful report, he determined to go to the aid of his men and deliver them from Circe's enchantment.

. . . Circe . . . touched each one with her wand.
Instantly, they were changed into swine.

As he strode forward, a handsome youth stopped him. It was none other than the god, Mercury, who had come to warn him of Circe's art and sorceries. When he saw that Ulysses was determined to rescue his men, Mercury gave him a sprig of a plant. This was a magic plant, and it would save Ulysses from Circe's power.

When Ulysses reached the palace, Circe, sure that she had another victim in her power, greeted him cordially. She gave him food and drink, and then, touching him with her wand, she cried, "Hence! Seek thy sty and wallow with thy friends!"

But Ulysses drew his sword and rushed upon the wicked Circe. She fell on her knees and begged for mercy.

"Where are my friends?" asked Ulysses. "Restore them to their human forms, if you do not wish to die!"

He made Circe promise that she would not harm him or his companions, and that she would give them everything they needed.

His men were changed back into their original forms. The rest of the men from Ulysses' ship were sent for, and all were feasted and magnificently entertained by Circe.

When the time came for them to leave, Circe, now completely their friend, did them a service without which they would all have lost their lives.

. . . Ulysses . . . rushed upon the wicked Circe.
She . . . begged for mercy.

In order to sail away from Circe's island, they had to pass the Island of the Sirens. These Sirens were sea nymphs whose singing was so beautiful that no one could resist them. When passing sailors heard the singing, they could not bear to leave. Indeed, the seamen would cast themselves into the sea to reach the Sirens, only to be drowned.

Circe told Ulysses to fill his sailors' ears with wax, before they approached within sound of the Sirens. He himself should instruct his men to tie him securely to the mast and not to release him from his bonds until they had passed the Sirens. Ulysses did as Circe had told him.

Soon, they drew near the Island of the Sirens. Over the water came the sound of their singing, so sweet, so utterly ravishing, that Ulysses could not stand it. He forgot everything in the world, only that he must go to them. He begged, he wept, and he stormed, demanding that his men untie him. But they, who could not hear the singing of the Sirens, remembered what he had told them. The more he implored, the tighter they tied his cords, and the faster they rowed.

Gradually, the fatal music grew fainter. When Ulysses could hear it no more, and they were safely past the danger, he signaled his men to remove the wax from their ears. Then they untied him. Ulysses thanked them for their faithfulness to him, and they went on their way.

PHAETON

A Boy in the Sun God's Chariot

THE ANCIENT GREEKS believed in gods who represented each of Nature's glories. Seeing the sun rise every morning they would say, "There goes the Sun God, Apollo, driving his great flaming chariot through the skies!"

Now Apollo, so the story goes, had a son on earth, named Phaeton. The lad's mother was Clymene, a beautiful nymph. Born of such beautiful parents, Phaeton grew up to be both proud and handsome. It was only natural that he should become indignant when some of his young friends scoffed at the story of his divine birth.

In fierce anger, Phaeton went to his mother and cried, "If I am truly the child of a god, give me some proof of it!"

"You are indeed the son of Apollo," said Clymene. "And if you wish to, you can prove it. You must journey far to the east, to the land where the sun rises. There you will find Apollo. Present yourself to him and let him tell you with his own lips who you are."

The headstrong youth did not delay an instant. He set forth at once. After many weeks' journey he found himself before the glorious Palace of the Sun. It was so magnificent, and it gleamed so brightly that the light was almost more than he could bear.

Phaeton entered the palace. At the end of a huge hall he saw Apollo, seated on a throne which glittered with diamonds. Around the Sun God's head gleamed golden rays.

On either side of the throne stood the attendants of Apollo: the Hour, the Day, the Month, the Year, and the Seasons. Spring was resplendent in a garland of flowers; Summer wore a garland of grain. Autumn stood there too, in a richly colored garment, his feet stained with the juice of the grape. Winter's face was pale, his garments were snow white, and his hair and beard were stiff with frost.

Seeing Phaeton at the end of the hall, Apollo beckoned him to approach and state his errand.

"Oh light of the world!" said Phaeton. "Apollo,

my father! Give me some proof, I beg you, by which I may be known as yours!"

Then Apollo, recognizing his son, laid aside the dazzling rays of the sun that shone around his head, stepped forward and embraced the handsome lad.

"Truly," he said, "you are my son and as a sign that this is so, ask for any gift you want. It shall be yours, I promise you."

Quick as a flash, Phaeton answered, "Oh, Father, just for one day let me drive your fiery chariot across the sky."

Apollo drew back and smote his forehead in despair.

"Oh, my son, I have promised rashly and you have made a most dangerous choice. Anything else in the world, I would gladly grant. You don't know what you ask! You are only a mortal, yet you ask to do what even the gods find difficult. None but myself may drive the flaming car of Day—not even Jupiter, whose terrible right hand hurls the thunderbolts. I must warn you of the dangers that would await you.

"The beginning of the journey is so steep that even my fiery steeds, fresh and strong as they are in the morning, can scarcely climb it. The middle is so high that even I grow dizzy with fear when I look down at the earth and sea below. The last part of the way goes down so steeply, that it takes all my strength not to fall headlong from my chariot.

"And all the time the heavens are turning above my head, carrying the stars in their sweeping movement, while the earth revolves in the opposite way beneath me.

"Perhaps you think that it is all a beautiful ride with the palaces and the temples of the gods along the way. Oh, no, my son! The path is beset by fearful monsters. You must pass the horns of the Bull; draw nigh to the Lion's paws. You must pass between

The beginning of the journey is so steep that even
my fiery steeds can scarcely climb it . . .

the claws of the Crab and the arms of the Scorpion.

"But worst of all, you have not the strength to hold in check the unruly steeds who pull the golden chariot of the sun. I can scarcely govern them myself. They are steeds born of flame, and fire breathes from their very nostrils.

"Oh, my son, take back your request while you can. You came to ask for proof that I am your father? If you could look into my heart, you would see proof enough of a father's love. Phaeton, choose anything in the world, the most precious thing that sea or earth contains, and I will not refuse you. Only do not ask to ride my chariot!"

But the hot-blooded youth would not be swayed. The pleas of Apollo fell on deaf ears. There was nothing for the Sun God to do but to keep his promise. In great fear, Apollo led Phaeton to the chariot.

The boy gazed in admiration at the magnificent car. It was made of gold and silver and precious stones which reflected the brightness of the sun. Joyous and impatient to be off, Phaeton sprang into the chariot.

Apollo covered his son's face with a powerful salve to withstand the great heat. He set the golden rays on Phaeton's head and proffered him these last words of advice. "Hold the reins tight. Do not use the whip, for the horses go fast enough of their own will. The important thing is to hold them in. Keep in the middle zone, for if you go too high, you will burn the heavenly dwellings of the gods, and if you go too low, you will set the earth on fire."

Phaeton thanked his heavy-hearted father and seized the reins. The chariot started forward with a rush. The horses soon felt that the load they pulled was much lighter than usual. Rushing headlong as they pleased, they left the Sun God's usual path.

Phaeton tried desperately to control the steeds but his strength was nothing to theirs. He looked down at the earth spreading beneath him and grew pale with terror. Soon enough he wished that he had never won his request—that he had never touched his father's flaming chariot!

The monsters of the sky stretched out their horrid claws toward him. In mortal fright, Phaeton lost his self-control. The reins dropped from his nerveless fingers. Now, with no controlling hand at the reins, the horses dashed off—first high up into the heavens, then down to the earth, spreading ruin as they ran.

As the chariot of the sun came close to the earth, great cities were consumed by the terrible heat; the fields of the earth were scorched and all the crops were destroyed. Mountain tops were left smoky; rivers were dried up. Destruction and terror filled the world.

Then Earth in her despair cried out to Jupiter, the king of the gods, to save her. And Jupiter, seeing that not only the earth, but the heavens themselves were in danger, stood up and gathered his lightning

bolts into his hand. He thundered and hurled a lightning bolt down from heaven straight toward Phaeton
in his chariot. Phaeton, his hair on fire, fell headlong
to the earth like a shooting star. Down he plunged
to his death, into a great river.

And so Phaeton, the willful boy who thought he
was mighty enough to drive the Sun God's own
chariot, had to be destroyed so that his vanity should
not result in the destruction of the world.

*. . . Jupiter . . . hurled a lightning bolt down from
heaven straight toward Phaeton . . .*

DAMON AND PYTHIAS

The Most Faithful of Friends

DAMON AND PYTHIAS were two young men who lived more than two thousand years ago, on the island of Sicily. Far and wide, Damon and Pythias were famed for their great friendship. Indeed, their names have come down to us to this day, as symbols of what true friendship means.

Syracuse, the city in which they lived, was ruled by a cruel and tyrannical king, named Dionysius. Dionysius cared nothing about the welfare of his people. His laws were harsh and brutal, and he enforced them pitilessly. But dreadful as were the hardships the people were forced to endure, they did not rebel for fear of the king's great and powerful army. No one even dared to complain, because anyone who was caught saying anything against the king was immediately punished.

But Damon and Pythias were brave men and refused to keep silent about the cruelties of their ruler. One day, one of the king's soldiers overheard Pythias talking against King Dionysius. He immediately arrested him and brought him before the king. But brave Pythias was not frightened. His hatred of King Dionysius was so great that he fearlessly told him to his face that he was a cruel and wicked tyrant! When Dionysius heard this, he became so furious that he ordered Pythias to be put in chains and thrown into prison immediately. He declared that in two weeks' time, Pythias would be executed.

When Damon discovered what had happened to his friend, he was heartbroken. He rushed to the prison to see Pythias. When he was brought before him, he said, "Oh, my dear friend, if only I could save you. I would willingly die myself, that you might live!"

Then Pythias answered, "I know that nothing can save me, and I am prepared to die. But there is one thought that torments me—what will happen to my sister and my old mother, when I am gone? If only I could go to see them before I die; if only I had a chance to make arrangements to take care of them, so they will not starve when I am no longer here!"

Then Damon went to King Dionysius and begged him to allow Pythias to go to see his mother once again before he died. "I will take the place of Pythias in prison," Damon said, "until he comes back. If Pythias is not here on the day of execution, kill me instead of him!"

Dionysius was astonished at this request. Never before had he seen or heard of anything like it. It so aroused his amazement and curiosity, that despite his anger at Pythias he agreed to it.

"But," he said to Damon, "I warn you, if your friend does not return on time, I will not spare your life!"

Damon went to his friend Pythias to tell him of his bargain with the king. Then Pythias set out to see his mother, and Damon was put in his place in prison.

More than a week went by. The day for the execution drew near and Pythias had not yet returned. "You see," said Dionysius, "your friend has tricked you. He will not come back here to be killed. You were a fool to take his place! He has run away and left you here to die instead of him."

But Damon's faith in his friend did not waver. "I know Pythias will return," he said, "and I am not afraid."

And indeed his faith was justified. Pythias had gone home and made arrangements so that his mother and sister would be able to live comfortably for many years. Then he had said a last farewell to his family, and set out to return to Syracuse.

But the way back was not easy. Robbers set upon him and stole his money. Then they tied him to a tree and left him there. No entreaty of his could persuade them to set him free. At last, after a desperate struggle, he managed to break his bonds.

Then he set off once more, as fast as possible, to reach Syracuse; for time was getting short. Day and night, he travelled without stopping. Hungry and exhausted, he stumbled through forests, swam across rivers, and crawled through swamps, in a desperate effort to get to Syracuse in time to save Damon's life.

But the day of execution dawned and Pythias had not yet returned.

"Ha!" sneered Dionysius, as Damon was being led into the prison courtyard for his execution. "Tell me, I pray you, where is your dear friend now?"

But Damon said, "If he has not come, I know it is through no fault of his own. I am glad to die in his place!"

Just as Damon finished saying these words, a pale, breathless man rushed into the courtyard. It was Pythias! Sobbing with relief, he threw his arms around Damon's neck saying, "Oh, my friend, thank God I am not too late!"

When Dionysius and his cruel soldiers saw this, even their hard hearts were moved.

"Never in all my life have I seen such faith and

*Sobbing with relief, he threw his arms around
Damon's neck saying, "Oh, my friend, thank
God I am not too late!"*

loyalty between friends," said Dionysius. "You may go free! I cannot destroy such a love as yours. Though I am a king and have treasure chests filled with gold and precious stones, though I rule over many people and command great armies, I would gladly give up all my money and power to have one friend like Damon or Pythias!"

PROSERPINE AND PLUTO

A Visit of Springtime to Earth

FAR DOWN UNDER the surface of the earth lay the lands of Pluto, God of the Underworld. Pluto, who despised light and avoided cheer, rarely left his dark and gloomy kingdom. But one day, he paid a short visit to the surface of the earth.

As he sped along the earth in his black chariot drawn by four black horses, he was seen by Cupid.

"What great good luck!" thought the mischievous God of Love, as he fitted an arrow to his bow. "Here's a target I may never get a chance at again!"

Cupid took careful aim and shot his arrow straight into Pluto's heart.

Now anybody hit by one of Cupid's arrows was sure to fall in love with the next person he saw. And the first person Pluto saw after being hit by the God of Love's arrow was Proserpine, the lovely daughter of Ceres, Goddess of the Harvest. Pluto encountered the maid as she was gathering lilies beside a gay, bubbling stream.

When Pluto saw her, he was overwhelmed with love. He swept Proserpine up in his arms and carried her off in his chariot. The terrified girl screamed for help, but there was no one to hear her cries.

Pluto struck the earth with his great three-pronged spear, and the ground opened up. Into the opening Pluto drove his plunging black horses, and in her struggles Proserpine dropped her sash. The earth closed again, while down, down, deep into the earth the chariot sped with Pluto and his beautiful prisoner.

Soon they arrived at Pluto's palace. The King of the Underworld spoke words of love to Proserpine. He begged her not to be afraid.

"You shall be my beloved," he said. "You shall reign as queen over all the realms of the dead."

But Proserpine only shook her head and wept. She would not look at Pluto; she would neither eat nor drink.

Far away, on the surface of the earth, Proserpine's mother, Ceres, was enveloped in despair. She searched the world over for her missing daughter.

One day, weary and sad, Ceres sat down beside a

Into the opening Pluto drove his plunging black horses, and in her struggles Proserpine dropped her sash.

river. The place she chose to rest was a fateful one. It was the very spot where Pluto had caused the earth to open, so that he could descend into his underworld kingdom with Proserpine!

A nymph, called Arethusa, who lived in the near-

by river had seen everything that had happened. She was terribly afraid of Pluto, and so she dared not tell Ceres that she had seen her daughter when Pluto disappeared into the earth with her. Instead, she lifted up the sash which Proserpine had dropped, and wafted it to the feet of her mother.

Ceres recognized it at once and cried out with grief at the sight of her daughter's sash. Now she knew that Proserpine was in the earth, but she did not know how she had got there or what had happened. In her grief and anger, she blamed the earth itself.

"Ungrateful soil!" cried Ceres. "I have given you richness and clothed you with greenery and nourishing grain. Is this how you repay me? Now no more shall you enjoy my favors."

In her terrible anger, Ceres sent too much rain, which killed the crops; then too much sun, which dried the fields. The leaves fell from the trees, cattle died, and plows broke in the sun-parched furrows. The poor earth suffered terribly.

Finally, Arethusa, the nymph, interceded for the land. "Goddess," she pleaded, "do not blame the land. Unwillingly did it open to let your daughter in. Pluto carried her off to be Queen of the Underworld. As my waters seeped through the earth, they saw her there. She is sad, but she is not afraid."

When Ceres heard this, she determined to get help. She quickly turned her chariot toward heaven and

Finally, Arethusa . . . interceded . . . "Goddess,"
she pleaded, "do not blame the land."

threw herself before the throne of Jupiter, the King of the Gods. She begged him to bring Proserpine back to earth—to force Pluto to give up her daughter.

Jupiter consented, but he was forced to make one condition. If Proserpine had not eaten anything while in the Underworld she could return; otherwise, she must stay in Pluto's Kingdom.

Mercury, the messenger of the gods, was then sent to Pluto with Jupiter's orders to return Proserpine to her mother.

Pluto could not refuse an order from Jupiter. But first, the wily Pluto offered Proserpine a pomegranate. Overjoyed at the thought of returning to Earth, and no longer afraid of Pluto, Proserpine started to bite into the fruit. In alarm, Mercury stopped her—but not before she had swallowed six pomegranate seeds.

Pluto was now able to demand that Proserpine spend six months of the year with him—one month for each seed she had swallowed.

And so it was arranged. For six months each year, Proserpine must leave her mother, Ceres, and be Pluto's queen.

During that time, Ceres is sad and unconcerned with the earth, she hides herself and wintry days come. Everything dies. It is winter.

At the end of six months, Proserpine comes back to her mother. She brings joy to Ceres and bright springtime returns to the earth.

THE CYCLOPS

The Death Battle of a Monster

ULYSSES, by his cleverness and courage, escaped from
many dangers as he made his way back to the Kingdom of Ithaca, after the fall of Troy.

Anxious to return to his beloved wife, Penelope,
and their little son, Telemachus, from whom he had
so long been separated, Ulysses sailed as quickly as
wind and sail would carry him toward home.

But raging storms battered the king's frail vessel,
and unfavorable winds drove the ship farther and
farther off its course.

Even the indomitable courage of Ulysses was put to
the test, as despair entered the hearts of his men.

It was with great relief that he finally sighted an island. Although it was unfamiliar, Ulysses thought he might be able to obtain fresh supplies there.

With a small group of men, Ulysses went ashore and set out to explore the island. With them, they carried a cask of wine as a friendship offering for whomever they might meet. They had not gone far when they chanced upon a large cave. Imagine their delight on entering it to find that it was piled high with all kinds of delicious food!

But the Greeks would scarcely have been so overjoyed had they known that the island was inhabited by a fierce race of giants called the Cyclopes. Each of these strange and hideous creatures had a single enormous eye set in the center of his forehead.

Ulysses and his men, however, did not know what manner of creatures these Cyclopes were, so their joy at finding the well-stocked cave was unrestrained. Weary and hungry, the mariners made a great fire, and began to eat heartily of the food they found in such abundance. Suddenly a vast shadow fell across the entrance to the cave, blocking out all sunlight! Polyphemus, the inhabitant of the cave, had returned, driving his flock of sheep before him.

A single glance at the one-eyed monster was enough to make the Greeks gasp in horror. Quaking with fear, they clustered together at the back of the cave while Polyphemus drove his flock through the entrance. Then, entering the cave himself, the Cyclops closed off the entrance with a stone so huge that twenty oxen could not have budged it.

As his one great eye accustomed itself to the dim light, Polyphemus suddenly became aware of his unexpected visitors.

"Who are you?" he roared, demanding to know in a voice that echoed like thunder, "And why come you here?"

Ulysses stepped forward. "We are Greeks," he answered humbly. "We are returning home from a war in which we have won much glory. In the name of the gods, we pray your hospitality."

The only answer Polyphemus gave was to reach out his enormous hands and seize two of Ulysses' men. As the unfortunate pair struggled in terror, the giant hurled them against the wall of the cave, killing them instantly.

In helpless horror the Greeks watched the giant devour their two unfortunate companions. Then the monster stretched himself out on the floor of the cave and went to sleep.

Ulysses jumped up and drew his sword. This was his chance to kill the Cyclops as he slept. But then he realized that all his men together did not have the strength to push away the stone that blocked the mouth of the cave. If they killed Polyphemus, they would all be buried alive!

When morning came, the giant again seized two of Ulysses' companions, killed them in the same way, and ate them. He then moved the enormous stone from the cave entrance, drove out his flock, and carefully replaced the stone. Polyphemus was taking no chances that Ulysses and his men would escape while he was gone.

But Ulysses' nimble mind had already set to work on a plan for escape. He ordered his men to take the huge bar of wood, big as the trunk of a tree, which the giant had used as a club, and whittle the end of it to a point with their swords. Then the Greeks hid it in a dark corner of the cave.

The only answer Polyphemus gave was to reach out his enormous hands and seize two of Ulysses' men.

When Polyphemus returned, once again they had to stand by helplessly while the giant murdered and devoured two more of their number. Then Ulysses approached the brute and offered him a bowl of wine drawn from the cask which they had carried from the ship. "Cyclops, this is good wine," said Ulysses.

The giant took the bowl, drained it at a gulp, and smacked his lips. "I find this good," said Polyphemus to Ulysses. "Let me have more. As your reward, I promise that you shall be the last one I devour. What is your name?"

"Noman is my name," said Ulysses, as he handed the giant another bowl of wine. Again and again, Ulysses filled the bowl, until the giant fell over in a drunken stupor, and lay snoring.

Then Ulysses, with four of his companions, lifted up the wooden club and plunged its point into the embers of the fire. When it became red hot, they thrust it deep into the Cyclops' eye, until the giant was completely blinded.

The howling monster filled the cave with such an outcry that the other Cyclopes heard him bellow. They rushed to his aid, demanding to know what was the matter.

"O friends," cried the giant, "I die and Noman has given the blow!"

The other Cyclopes answered, "Well, then, if no man has given the blow, it is a stroke from the gods

and there is nothing we can do. You must bear it."
And they left.

The infuriated Polyphemus tried to catch Ulysses
and his men, but as the giant was now blind the
Greeks found it easy to elude his groping hands.

Next morning, the Cyclops again rolled away the
stone to let his flock out to pasture. The only way
the blind man could prevent his prisoners from escaping at the same time was by his sense of touch. He
planted himself at the entrance of the cave to feel
each of his sheep as they went through, to make sure
no man was among them.

But Ulysses had foreseen this, too.

He had spent most of the night tying the rams together in groups of threes. Next morning each of the
Greeks, clinging desperately with hands and knees,
swung himself face up under the middle one of the
rams. As each trio of animals walked out of the cave,
the blind and vengeful giant felt their backs and
sides. But the Cyclops did not think to reach under
them.

So Ulysses and his few remaining companions escaped. They reached their ship, where their other
friends were anxiously awaiting them and pushed off
from shore. When they were at what seemed a safe
distance, Ulysses shouted: "Cyclops, the gods have
punished you well for your terrible deeds. Now you
may know it was Ulysses who blinded you!"

In a towering rage, Polyphemus tore a huge stone from the mountainside and hurled it in the direction of the ship. The waves caused by the enormous boulder drove the ship inland. His companions implored Ulysses not to taunt the giant further. So Ulysses and his men bent to their oars with all their might and soon were at a safe distance from the island.

In nine years of war, Ulysses had never had a more narrow escape.

In a towering rage, Polyphemus tore a huge stone
and hurled it in the direction of the ship.

THE RETURN OF ULYSSES

A King Metes Out Retribution

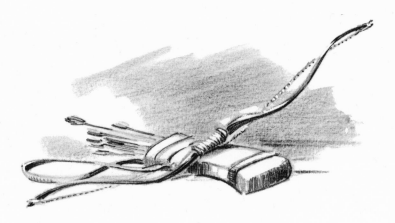

WHEN ULYSSES had set forth for Troy to help the Greeks in their war, he was a young man. He found it hard to part from his beautiful wife, Penelope, and his baby son, Telemachus. Even so, he thought that only a year or so would pass before he would be able to return home.

But it took nine years to win the Trojan War. And because Ulysses had angered certain gods, he was forced to wander for eleven more years before he finally reached his home.

During the twenty long years that Ulysses was gone, Penelope had remained faithful to him. She did her best to keep the affairs of their kingdom in order. But after a while, the neighboring princes, as well as the men of her own court, convinced that Ulysses would never return, pressed her to choose one of them for a husband, to be king of Ithaca.

For a long time, Penelope put them off. The suitors became more and more insistent. They lorded it over the palace and the people, as if they were the rulers already. Penelope was helpless to hold them in check. They made the palace and the country poor with their spendthrift ways. Things got so bad that Penelope, fearful for her son's life, sent him away. He searched for his father, but in vain.

Meanwhile, the suitors were angry that Penelope did not make her choice. For years, she had put them off, saying that when she had finished a certain piece of tapestry which she was weaving on her loom, she would choose a husband from among them.

Day by day, and year by year, she wove at her loom, but at night she secretly unraveled her work. Finally, however, the suitors would wait no longer.

Things were in this state when Ulysses, having lost all his men and ships, landed alone in his city. Minerva, the Goddess of Wisdom, who favored Ulysses, knew that the wicked suitors would be far from glad to see Ulysses return. They had wanted his kingdom for too long to allow him to recover it. They would surely kill him.

So Minerva changed Ulysses into an old beggar. While in this disguise, he met an old swineherd named Emmaeus who had been a faithful servant of Ulysses during all the long years of his absence. Emmaeus did not know who the old beggar was, but he received him kindly.

Minerva also advised Ulysses' son, Telemachus, who was now a young man, to return to his country. Telemachus, knowing that his own life was in danger from the suitors, first went to the hut of Emmaeus. He sent Emmaeus to his mother at the palace to tell her of his arrival.

While Emmaeus was gone, Ulysses told his son who he really was. At that, Minerva restored to Ulysses his own manly good looks, but he kept the clothes of a beggar.

Telemachus wept with joy to see his father, for whom he had yearned so many years. And Ulysses was overjoyed to hold his son in his arms at last.

They took counsel together as to how they should overcome the powerful suitors who had taken over their kingdom, and how they would punish them.

They made a plan. Telemachus and Ulysses went to the palace—Telemachus, as the young prince coming home, and Ulysses disguised as an old beggar, a sort of wandering storyteller.

As Ulysses entered the courtyard of his palace, unrecognized even by his wife, his old dog, Argus, was lying in the yard. Argus had been too weak to move, but suddenly he raised his head, his ears stood up, and he was all joy, for he knew his master. Lucky for Ulysses that few people were around to see this sight!

In the palace hall, they found the usual scene of riotous feasting. The suitors pretended to greet Telemachus with joy, but they were furious that their plots to kill him had gone awry.

This was the day, however, when Penelope had finally been forced to promise to choose a husband. The suitors were to contest for her hand by a trial of skill with the bow and arrow. Twelve rings were set up against the wall. The man who succeeded in shooting an arrow into every one of the twelve rings was to have the queen as his bride.

There was a great bow in the palace armory which had belonged to Ulysses. This bow was to be used in the contest. Telemachus, in accordance with the plans he had made with Ulysses, allowed only this weapon to be brought into the hall. His excuse was that, in the heat of the contest, fighting might break out amongst the suitors.

They got ready for the contest, but when they tried to bend the great bow to attach the string, no one could do it. First Telemachus, then each of the suitors in turn tried to bend the bow, but without success.

Then Ulysses spoke up. "Let me try," he said. "Beggar though I am, I was once a soldier, and maybe

there is some strength left in my limbs."

The suitors laughed at his insolence. They wanted the beggar thrown out.

But Telemachus calmed them. He pretended that it would be amusing to watch the beggar struggle, and he handed the bow to Ulysses.

Then Ulysses, with great ease, fitted the string to the bow. While everyone watched in astonishment, he shot twelve arrows, one after another, into the twelve rings.

Then he fitted another arrow to his bow. "Now for another mark!" he said. And with that, he aimed for the most overbearing of all the suitors. The arrow pierced the man's throat, and he died instantly.

*While everyone watched in astonishment, he shot
twelve arrows . . .*

The suitors rushed for their weapons, but the doors had been locked . . .

Now Telemachus, Emmaeus, and another faithful follower sprang to arms. The suitors rushed for their weapons, but the doors had been locked by Emmaeus, and they were helpless.

Ulysses then told them that he was the King of Ithaca himself, whose land they had invaded, whose riches they had spent, whose wife and son they had persecuted for so many years.

They were all banished, and Ulysses was once more king in his own land. He was reunited with his beautiful wife Penelope and both their hearts rejoiced at their new-found happiness.

CUPID AND PSYCHE

The Immortal Lovers

LONG AGO, THERE lived a king who had three daughters. Two of them were very pretty, but the youngest was the most beautiful one of all. Her name was Psyche.

She was so beautiful that her fame spread. People came from far and near just to see her. Many people thought she must be a goddess, and they scattered flowers in her path and worshiped her.

When Venus, the Goddess of Love and Beauty, saw this, she was very angry.

"Shall a mortal girl take away from me my homage and honor?" she cried.

Then turning to her son, Cupid, she said, "Go now to earth and strike Psyche with one of your arrows and cause her to fall in love with the most unworthy of men. That shall be her punishment."

Cupid set forth to do his mother's bidding. He carried with him two jars from his mother's garden. One contained bitter water, which brought sadness, and the other, sweet water, which brought joy. When he came to Psyche's room, where she lay asleep, he sprinkled a few drops of the bitter water over her lips.

Psyche opened her lovely eyes. At the sight of them, Cupid became so confused that he wounded himself with his own arrow.

Now he was stricken with a deep love for her. Quickly, he tried to undo the harm he had done her, and sprinkled the sweet water of joy over her. Then he fled.

Psyche did not see him, for he had made himself invisible. But Cupid had not only seen Psyche, he had pierced himself with his own arrow of love. From now on, he would love no one but her.

His mother had sent him to punish Psyche. Now he had fallen in love with her. His mother's anger would be terrible if she found out. What could he do? He had to flee from the sight of his beloved Psyche.

From then on, however, Psyche derived no joy from her beauty. For Venus, in her jealousy, arranged it so that no man dared come forth to ask the hand of

Psyche in marriage. Her two sisters were married to kings, but Psyche grew lonelier every day.

As time went on, her father and mother, saddened at the unhappiness of their beloved daughter, felt that they must do something to help her. They consulted an oracle and asked for advice. The oracle told them that Psyche would marry no ordinary mortal, but a monster whom no one could resist. This monster was waiting for her on top of a high mountain.

The dreadful decree of the fortuneteller filled the king and queen with grief.

Psyche only said, "Why are you all so sad now? You should have been sad when people paid homage to my beauty and called me as lovely as Venus; for

. . . Cupid became so confused that he wounded himself with his own arrow.

now I see that because of this, I am suffering this cruel fate. As for me, my life is so lonely, I care not what happens to me. Take me to the mountain."

So, amid weeping and sorrow, Psyche was led to the top of the mountain and left there alone.

As Psyche stood there, expecting a terrible fate, a gentle breeze blew softly and whispered to her not to fear. It was Zephyrus the kindly West wind which Cupid had sent to comfort her. Suddenly it lifted her up as if she were on wings and carried her away. Softly, it set her down in a beautiful valley. She could not understand what was happening, but, worn out from all her fears, she fell asleep.

When she awoke, she looked around her and found herself in the grounds of a magnificent palace. As she gazed in amazement, a voice spoke to her, saying, "Noble and most beautiful princess, all that you see is yours. We are your servants and shall obey all your commands. Your room awaits you, with a bed of down. Rest yourself. Then, when you wish to eat, supper will be prepared for you."

Psyche did as the voice told her. After she had bathed and rested, she sat down in the dining alcove, where a table appeared as if from nowhere, laden with the choicest foods and wines. Soft music played for her while she ate.

When night came, Psyche heard the soft fluttering of wings, and footsteps came to her side bringing her husband to her. She could not see him, for it was dark, but he spoke to her with such tender words that she could not help but love him. Then, before dawn, he left her.

All day she yearned for his return, and, with the darkness, he came back to her. She begged him to stay, to let her see him, but he would not consent.

"Beloved Psyche," he said. "Do not try to see me. Why should you wish to? Do you doubt my love? If you saw me, maybe you would begin to fear me, for maybe you would adore me as a god. I would rather that you loved me as an equal than adored me as a god. Trust and love me."

Psyche was calmed by these words. She was content, for she loved her husband, and she loved her beautiful palace.

But after a while, Psyche grew lonely for her parents and her sisters. She knew that they thought she had been carried off by a monster, yet here she was, safe and sound. If she could only let them know. If she could only see them!

When her husband came at night, she poured out her trouble to him, and finally, with a heavy heart, he agreed to let her two sisters visit her.

The same gentle breeze carried them to her. Psyche was overjoyed to see them. She greeted them with kisses and showered them with gifts.

When her sisters saw the beautiful palace that

Psyche lived in, full of priceless treasures so much richer than theirs, they became envious of her good fortune. They asked her all sorts of questions, especially about her husband.

"Where is he?" they asked. "Why do we not see him?"

At first, Psyche tried to pretend that he was temporarily away from home. But finally, she confessed the truth—that she had never set eyes on him, that he only came to her at night.

"O, Psyche!" they cried. "Do not be deceived. Remember the oracle's prophecy, that you would be carried off by a monster? You have never seen your husband. Why does he hide himself from you? It stands to reason that he means to harm you. He is a monster and he means to fatten you just to devour you.

"You must do as we say. Prepare for yourself a lamp and a sharp knife. When he comes to you at night, wait until he has fallen asleep. Then light your lamp and look at him. You will see for yourself that he is a monster. If he is, quickly cut off his head, and free yourself from his imprisonment."

Psyche would not listen to such ideas. She insisted that her husband loved her, and that he was not what they said. But after they returned home, their words began to torment her. She began to wish she had some proof with which she could allay their terrible suspicions.

Their words began to torment her.

Finally, her curiosity and fears got the better of her, and she prepared the lamp and the knife as her sisters had told her.

That night, when her husband had fallen asleep, she got up quietly and brought the lamp over to the couch where he lay.

As the lamp lit up the couch, she saw, not an ugly monster, but Cupid, the God of Love himself—the most beautiful and charming of the gods.

His golden curls, his face more beautiful than the springtime, and the delicate wings which grew on his shoulders, filled her with adoration and love. She stood transfixed, forgetting everything but her love for him.

Poor Psyche leaned over him. Her hand trembled and a drop of hot oil from the lamp she was holding, fell on the sleeping Cupid. Instantly he awoke.

He looked into her eyes with reproach and sadness.

"Oh, Psyche," he said. "Is this how you repay me? I have loved you tenderly with all my heart and soul. Yet you would sooner believe the words of your sisters than my acts of love. Love cannot live with suspicion. I leave you now forever."

With these words, Cupid arose and flew away.

Psyche, in despair, tried to follow him. But it was no use. Now, indeed, she was lonely. Nothing meant anything to her but her love for Cupid, and she made up her mind that she must find him and beg his forgiveness. She set forth, not really knowing where to go, but hoping that somehow she would find him.

Day and night she searched for him, without success. Then, one day, she came to a beautiful temple.

"Perhaps my lord lives in this lovely place," she thought.

As she entered the temple, she found piles of corn and barley grains in great disorder, strewn all about. Immediately, she set to work and sorted out the grains in their proper places. As she was engaged in this work, the goddess Ceres, whose temple this was, spoke to her.

"Oh Psyche," she said, "truly I pity you. I cannot help you, for Venus is angry with you. But perhaps

. . . *when her husband had fallen asleep, she got up quietly and brought the lamp over to the couch where he lay.*

if you go to her and try to win her favor by modesty
and willingness to serve her, she will forgive you
and restore your husband to you."

So Psyche, willing to do anything to win back her
husband, went to the temple of Venus to do as Ceres
had advised.

Venus received her with anger. "So finally you
come to me, faithless girl," she cried. "Finally, you
remember that I am your mistress. You are so foolish
and ugly that the only way you can be worthy of
your lover is by diligence and industry as a housewife. I will see what kind of a housewife you are!"

So saying, she led Psyche to a large storehouse
filled with a tremendous pile of wheat, barley, millet,
beans, and lentils—all mixed together.

"Separate all these grains. See that you get it done
before evening," she said. And with that, she left
Psyche to her work.

Psyche gazed hopelessly at the impossible task.
How could she possibly succeed? What could she do?

While she sat, not knowing what to do, a tiny ant
appeared. He had been sent by Cupid, who knew of
her plight. The ant, followed by a whole army of ants,
set to work. All day long, they worked, separating
each of the seeds, grain by grain.

When evening came, and Venus appeared, she was
astonished to see the work accomplished.

"This is no work of yours, wicked one!" she cried.

And she threw Psyche a piece of black bread for her supper.

The next morning, Venus appeared again.

"I have another task for you," she said. "See there, on the other side of the river is a flock of sheep. Their fleece is all of pure gold. Go and bring me a sample of the golden fleece from each one of their backs."

Then she left.

Psyche prepared to do as she was bid. As she stood on the bank of the rushing river, about to cross, she heard a voice speaking to her.

"Unfortunate girl," it said. "Do not try to cross the rough stream to the field where the golden sheep are grazing. For they are sheep of the sun. They are filled with a wild rage to devour mortals. Wait until they become calm, when they lie down to rest in the shade at noontime. Then you can cross the river, and you will find the woolly gold of their fleece sticking to the bushes."

In gratitude, Psyche heeded the warning and did as she was told.

When evening came, she was ready for Venus, with her arms full of the golden wool.

Now Venus was angrier than ever, for she know that Psyche could not have succeeded without help.

"I know full well that you could not have done this unaided. Therefore I am not convinced that you are a good worker. I have yet another task for you.

*. . . how to persuade the ferryman to row her
across the river to the dead.*

"Take this box to Proserpine, Queen of the Under-world, and say to her, 'My mistress, Venus, desires you to send her some of your beauty, for in tending her sick son, she has lost some of her own.' "

Psyche now had no hope at all. For who had ever gone to the Kingdom of the Dead and returned?

Then she heard a voice speaking to her. "Two times you have been saved. Have confidence! Do what I tell you, and you will accomplish this task, too."

Then the voice told her how to escape all the dangers on the road, how to calm the three-headed dog which guards the Palace of Proserpine, and how to persuade the ferryman to row her across the river to the dead and to bring her back again.

"But when Proserpine has filled your box with beauty, as Venus requested, do not open the box . . . not under any circumstances!"

Psyche did as the voice directed her and made her way to Queen Proserpine. The queen fulfilled her request and gave her back the box filled with beauty.

Psyche returned from inside the earth, glad to be back under the open sky once more. However, instead of being happy, she began to feel sadder than ever.

"Venus tells me I am no longer lovely. How will I ever win back my beloved husband unless I am beautiful? Of what use is all my work unless he loves me? Here is this box filled with a goddess's beauty. I will take just a little of it to help me."

So she carefully opened the box, not knowing that it contained a different kind of beauty than she had imagined. To Proserpine, Queen of the Dead, death was a sort of beauty, and that was what she had put in the box.

The sleep of death overcame Psyche, and there on the hillside she lay, motionless.

All this time, Cupid had been locked up in a room by his mother, Venus. But now, when he saw Psyche lying as if dead on the hillside, he escaped from the room where his mother had kept him prisoner, and flew to the spot where she lay. He leaned down and kissed her. His divine kiss overcame the deathly sleep, and Psyche opened her eyes.

"Oh my Psyche, once more you have almost lost everything because of your curiosity," he said. "Finish the task which my mother gave you. Bring her the box into which I have returned the sleep which overcame you. Then leave the rest to me."

Cupid flew up to the heavens. He presented himself before the throne of Jupiter, and pleaded fervently for Psyche's life. Jupiter was so moved by Cupid's love for Psyche that he prevailed on Venus to give her consent to their marriage.

So Psyche was carried to heaven where she was given a cup of ambrosia to drink. This made her immortal, like the gods; and so Cupid and Psyche were united forever.

*. . . he saw Psyche lying as if dead on the hillside
. . . He leaned down and kissed her.*

PERSEUS

The Quest for the Gorgon's Head

LONG AGO IN ancient Greece, the King of Argos was told by an oracle that one day his daughter's son would kill him. As Danaë was his only daughter, he decided that he would outwit the oracle by preventing her from ever becoming a mother. Therefore he shut her up in a tower and kept her under lock and key with heavy guards posted night and day around the tower.

But the gods laughed at his feeble efforts and Jupiter himself decided to visit the beautiful prisoner. This he did in a shower of gold and made love to the Princess Danaë.

When the king heard that his daughter had had a

son by Jupiter, he became exceedingly fearful. He did not dare have his own daughter and grandson put to death but he did something equally cruel and heartless.

He caused them to be placed in a small boat without any provisions; the boat was towed out to sea and left to the mercies of the winds and the waves. Then the king banished them from his mind—quite confident they would soon starve to death or be drowned.

However, the gods did not forget Danaë and her infant son, Perseus. They sent swift winds and swifter currents and the next morning the tiny boat drifted close to an island. There they were rescued by Dictys, a kind fisherman who took them to his home and cared for them for many years.

Perseus grew into a handsome and fearless youth who was both gentle and strong. By the time he was fifteen, he excelled all the other young men on the island, and King Polydectes, who ruled there, grew jealous.

He was not only jealous of Perseus' good looks and endearing ways, but he was jealous of him because he wanted Perseus' mother for himself. But she loved the good fisherman, and the king decided that if he could get rid of Perseus, then he could force Danaë to marry him. And so he devised a plot which he was certain would end in Perseus' death.

All the young men of the island were invited to a great feast at the palace. As was the custom, each brought with him a magnificent present for the king. Because Perseus was poor and had nothing beyond what the kind Dictys shared with him and his mother, he was unable to bring a gift.

But Perseus had something very special to offer and on this the king counted, for he knew Perseus was a proud and honorable youth. Perseus had his courage and his skill and these he told the king he would gladly put at his disposal.

The crafty king seized on this and commanded Perseus, "Go then, and prove thy courage! Bring to me the head of Medusa the Gorgon, for this I desire above all else."

Then Perseus realized that the king planned his death for no one had yet set eyes upon the Gorgons and lived. Nevertheless he went at once to do the king's bidding although he well knew he might never return.

The Gorgons were three terrible sisters who lived on a rocky island in the middle of the sea. Above their waists they looked like women, except that in place of hair their heads were covered by horrible, writhing snakes with poisonous fangs and darting forked tongues. Below their waists, the Gorgons' bodies were those of dragons; their scales and claws were made of brass and iron—with one thrash of her tail, a Gorgon could kill a man instantly.

Medusa was the most frightful of the three sisters

. . . the boat was towed out to sea and left to the
mercies of the winds and the waves.

The Gorgons were three terrible sisters who lived on a rocky island in the middle of the sea.

for whoever looked upon her face was turned to stone.

When Perseus set forth on his journey, the gods came to his assistance. The Goddess Minerva lent him her bright shining shield which shone like a golden mirror, and her magic pouch. Mercury lent him his winged sandals which enabled him to fly through the air, and also his curious crooked sword.

First Perseus flew to the end of the world where the three Gray Sisters lived. They alone knew the secret of where the Gorgons could be found. These weird old hags had only one eye and one tooth between them.

The sisters would not tell Perseus where the Gorgons lived, but as he stood there trying to persuade them, they began to quarrel amongst themselves. One said to the other, "Give me the eye, it is my turn." Another cried angrily, "No, no, give it to me, for it is my turn!" Yet another cried, "Give me the tooth, that I may chew."

As one tried to snatch an eye or a tooth from the other, Perseus saw his chance and seized them both and would not give them back until the sisters had told him how to find the Island of the Gorgons.

Once again the winged sandals carried him swiftly through the air and Perseus came to the Island of the Gorgons. He heard the clanking of their tails and saw the glitter of their brass claws. But he knew enough not to look at them directly. Instead he gazed into Minerva's shield and he saw there the reflection of the three Gorgons—fast asleep.

They were indeed terrible creatures and the snakes intertwined about their heads darted their flickering tongues and hissed viciously at the approaching Perseus.

Still looking into the shield, Perseus swooped down

and with a quick stroke of the wonderful sword, he struck off Medusa's head and thrust it into the magic pouch. Just as Medusa's sisters woke, he sprang into the air.

With horrible cries they tried to seize him, but Perseus sped away swift as an arrow and with the winged sandals he was soon out of their reach.

On his way home he stopped off at an island to rest and enjoy himself after all the horrors he had been through. A great festival of sports was being held there and Perseus competed in the discus throwing. His first throw went so far that his discus landed among the spectators.

Perseus was shocked to learn that it had killed a visiting king who was sitting in the royal enclosure. But he was even more horrified to find that the king was none other than his own grandfather who had left his kingdom because he feared the now-grown Perseus might return.

After many strange adventures Perseus reached home where his mother received him with tears of joy. While he had been away, Danaë had been treated very cruelly by King Polydectes because she could not find it in her heart to love him.

Full of anger, Perseus laid aside his helmet and sandals, and taking the magic pouch he went to the palace. Now Polydectes had long thought him dead. Great was his astonishment at seeing Perseus and he

. . . before the king realized what he was doing,
Perseus . . . held it on high . . . crying,
"Behold Medusa's Head!"

cried scornfully, "Aha, Perseus! So you have failed in your mission and returned without Medusa's head!"

"Not so," answered the brave Perseus. "I have slain the Gorgon." And before the king realized what he was doing, Perseus drew the head swiftly from the pouch and held it on high before the king's eyes, crying, "Behold Medusa's head!"

Polydectes grew pale with terror, but he had no power to move—for in a moment he was changed into lifeless stone. Everyone rejoiced that the cruel Polydectes was dead and even greater was the rejoicing when Perseus proclaimed the kindly Dictys as king who, in turn, made Danaë his queen.

As for Perseus, he went back to the land of his birth and there he ruled as King of Argos.

HART

PUBLISHING

COMPANY